bel
6.76

SAMUEL NOVEY, M.D.

THE SECOND LOOK

The Reconstruction of Personal History in Psychiatry and Psychoanalysis

FOREWORD BY BERTRAM D. LEWIN, M.D.

THE JOHNS HOPKINS PRESS

BALTIMORE

FOREWORD

Colleagues and friends of Samuel Novey, still lamenting his too early death, are offered the consolation of an after-message by this book, which reflects so well his quality of mind and character. In his life, contemplation and practice were harmoniously blended; encyclopedic interest and knowledge pervaded his professional studies and actions. In his view, behavior was grounded in knowledge, and experience was not sufficient until it was scrutinized and integrated into what was known. Erudition was constantly brought to bear on practice; exceptional gifts as a clinical observer were employed to test the products of reflection and were guided by exceptionally keen critical judgment that could not be propitiated by a "bright idea."

But Samuel Novey had many truly bright ideas. His mind—intuitive, informed, contemplative—merits a rather old-fashioned word: *philosophic*. It was resonant with the minds of the old doctors of the past, who knew Locke and Condorcet and saw medicine as part of the history of ideas, saw it against the greater background of epistemology and moral philosophy. Accordingly, Novey did not see psychiatry and psychoanalysis as guild disciplines to be governed finally by professional boards and contemporary professional organizations. They were, for him, manifestations of man's understanding of himself and of his place in nature and history, fields in which the larger workings of nature, history, knowledge, and ethics were themselves seeking solution.

Medical students are taught to take the patient's "history," to record the facts of the past according to conventional practice. Since pertinence is determined by utility, the records and the attention vary with the medical specialty; the "history" of a broken leg is not the history of the same patient's chronic headaches. The traditional psychiatric history is determined by the same considerations of use and usage. Students make these records in good faith, first assuming and then discovering for themselves the value of this ancient procedure. Their eye is on what is called "diagnosis," from which treatment is assumed to be a corollary.

Psychoanalytic "histories" have a different quality. History gathering is intimately and immediately linked with therapy, in many ways indistinguishably. As part of therapy, psychoanalysts not only take note of what the patient remembers, but also try to deduce, or "construct," the parts of the history concealed from the patient's consciousness by amnesias, particularly those which are regularly present as *infantile* amnesias. Psychoanalysts are consequently especially interested in ways of justifying their inferences and have given the matter much attention. Novey shares this interest of his psychoanalytic colleagues, but he is also aware that the conventional procedures and methods imply a philosophy and the broader issues of historical method, definition of purpose, valuation, and general epistemological and moral-philosophic problems. From his special experience in the law courts, he learned of the value and nature of evidence.

Thucydides is said to have been impressed by the uses which his medical contemporaries could make of the anamnesis and to have found justification for the recording of events in the hope that the records might enable future generations to avoid the errors of their ancestors. This idea of the corrective influence of historical study enters into the psychiatrist's and psychoanalyst's therapeutic use of the patient's personal history. The difficulty of eliminating myth and prejudice, preconception, and censored distortion is known to the general historian and the psychoanalyst alike.

The titles of Novey's chapters indicate how aware he was of the general—and the special—problems. There is a major chapter on The Technical Use of History in Treatment, but before this are background chapters titled The Function of History, The Meaning of History, and The Significance of the Actual Historical Events. In all of these, the thoughts of professional historians are brought to bear on special psychoanalytic problems. Indeed, a great merit is Novey's insistence on sharp specification. The special problems are not stated as abstractions; his great clinical experience enables him to furnish telling, concrete instances. The reader is left in no doubt as to the reality and appearance of the problems in everyday life and practice.

Novey's deep appreciation of the pervasiveness of ethical values in the daily practice of psychoanalysts, in particular, often unsuspectedly in what seem to be simple matters of technique, leads him again to supply concrete and precise clinical illustrations. It is this awareness no less than his deep sense of the need of testing observations and scientific concepts—in other words his respect for truth and the observer's talent—which are the ingredients that warrant the characterization "philosophic," cherishing all knowledge.

The refreshing breadth of these chapters is not their sole virtue. Professional colleagues will find not only familiar problems but suggested solutions, balanced consideration—certainly the new light of sound thinking. Whether his propositions and arguments compel agreement or stimulate thought in the reader, their clear statement will surely arouse his respect, his gratitude, and finally, the regret which all of us share.

BERTRAM D. LEWIN
Pipersville, Pennsylvania

August 9, 1967

PREFACE

This book is the distillate of a lifetime of observation and thought, and it reflects my husband's search to explain intriguing life experiences—his own experiences, my experiences, and those of friends and patients. It was completed just before his death in May, 1967. While examining his papers during the preparation of the manuscript for publication, I encountered a handwritten sheet entitled, "How I Became Interested in This Subject." He mentioned, first of all, his study of the writing of Sigmund Freud, who originally believed that traumatic childhood events reported by patients had actually occurred, and then discovered that many of these reported events were only wish-fulfilling phantasies, the recall of which was essential to cure. To Dr. Novey, this was an arresting phenomenon, stimulating a search to find answers to some of the questions it raised. Thus, he developed the conviction central to his book—that a patient cannot report an actual event which occurred in his past; he can only report his present inner experience of that event. In so doing, under favorable circumstances, he may initiate far-reaching changes within himself.

A personal experience of great importance to him occurred in 1945. Starting out from our home in Baltimore for a weekend in Southern Maryland, Dr. Novey was impelled to go on, and he impulsively drove to Rocky Mount, North Carolina, parking his car in front of a small house which he discovered to be his birthplace. It was here that he experienced the poignant feelings described in the chapter entitled "Why Some Patients Conduct Actual Investigations of Their Biographies." This experience, plus those of valued friends and patients, provided the nucleus of papers with which he began this book, and he wrote, "My primary interest is in the clinical situation. The clinical observations have papers built around them."

His observations were by no means confined to his own work, and in the examples he used in the above chapter, none of the patients he described had the same analyst. The purpose of this was to prevent his thinking being unduly affected by his own or another's personal bias.

As time went on, Dr. Novey began to interest himself in what other disciplines could contribute to psychoanalytic understanding of this problem. (He commented that psychoanalysts had traditionally been interested in the reverse.) He set about acquainting himself with what historians and philosophers of history had to say. Such books as W. H. Walsh's *Philosophy of History* impressed him deeply. He agreed with W. H. Walsh's view that each historian approaches the past with his own philosophical ideas and that this decisively affects the way in which he interprets it. This, Dr. Novey believed, was true of psychiatrists and psychoanalysts as well. This relativistic view played an important part in the development of his paper "The Sense of Reality of the Analyst as Historian." He became aware that much of what psychiatry has taken for granted as "history" is actually unsupported by facts. Continuing his searching examination of the authenticity of biographical data, he reviewed psychological and neurophysiological studies regarding memory, and he searched through Wigmore and other legal writers for information about the validation of evidence. He concluded that while historical data derived from patients is of great value in treatment, theory-making based upon such information is valid only if it constitutes a formulation of what people experience in the present. It is not valid if used as evidence of "what actually happens."

In the months before his death, Dr. Novey was concerned about the growing tendency among psychotherapists to carry out their work without sufficient regard for the case history, avowedly in the interest of concentrating on the interaction of patient and therapist. "The therapeutic process," he wrote "is an interaction in the present, conceptually bound to the historical past of the patient. If the patient and his problems are to be understood, history is to be understood, and yet there is little general interest in the broad topic of history throughout the field of personality study." In his chapter on the technical use of history in treatment, and elsewhere throughout the book, he has demonstrated how "the reconstruction of history by patient and therapist underwrites the living nature of history as a continuing part of the therapeutic process itself." These, then, are some of the strands which are woven into this book.

The original title of the book was *The Reconstruction of History as an Integral Part of Dynamic Psychotherapy and Psychoanalysis.* While searching for a shorter title, we discovered a tape recording of a panel discussion which took place at the April, 1967, meeting of the Maryland Psychological Association. At this time, Dr. Novey discussed the modification of behavior through conditioning techniques with Dr. Leo Walder and Dr. Herbert Weingartner. The use of these techniques represents a form of treatment of emotional disorders (now frequently referred to as "behavioral disorders") which is at present a center of interest among psychologists and many psychiatrists. Dr. Novey, while recognizing the usefulness of behavioral therapy, expressed the belief that basing an understanding of the modification of behavior on the building and unbuilding of patterns through conditioning techniques overlooked the importance of the inner experience of one's life history. Alterations of the memory of prior experience, he thought, played an important part in changes of personality patterns. When asked how the psychoanalysis could bring about modification of behavior, Dr. Novey replied:

> It would have to be looked at in the context of that person's relationship with the therapist. I would guess the sustaining force of this relationship, the possibility of examining one's self with another, sufficiently reduces the level of anxiety so as to permit the possibility of exploring areas that otherwise for most people would be impossible to explore. Why does the exploration itself make any remarkable difference? This is my behavioral sense of it, that each of us goes around with a curriculum vitae, with a sense of who we are, where we've been, where we're going. This is in people who are having difficulties, an unfortunate one. Suppose they get together with someone and gain what I might call perspective, get *a second look.* Get the view of prior events to be looked at again—not prior events as they happened, but today's view of those events. If this is modified, I think there is an accompanying modification of the people themselves.

Dr. Weingartner asked him, "Do you feel that behavioral theory leaves something unobserved, some important human event? Are we missing things?" To this Dr. Novey replied, "Yes! I think so! The world of my experience is important, and it is not all to be described in behavioral terms."

I should like to acknowledge the contributions of several people to this book. Two of my husband's close friends, Dr. Hans Loewald and Dr. Eugene Meyer III, who read and criticized his writings through the years, assisted me with decisions related to this publication. Dr. and Mrs. William Holden and Dr. and Mrs. Francis McLaughlin assisted with the editing of the manuscript. Dr. Holden also assisted substantially with the Glossary. Mrs. Dorothy Mulcahy, Dr. Novey's secretary for many years, worked closely with him on the preparation of all of the chapters. Mrs. Olga Hutchins and Mrs. Charlotte Miller contributed valuable stenographic assistance.

RIVA NOVEY, M. D.

November, 1967
Baltimore, Maryland

ACKNOWLEDGMENT

I wish to thank the editors of several journals for permission to publish, with certain changes, the following:

"The Meaning of History in Psychiatry and Psychoanalysis," *British Journal of Medical Psychology* (1962) 35:263.

"The Significance of the Actual Historical Event in Psychiatry and Psychoanalysis," *British Journal of Medical Psychology* (1964), 37: 279.

"Why Some Patients Conduct Actual Investigations of Their Biographies," *Journal of the American Psychoanalytic Associations,* Vol. 14, No. 2 (April, 1966).

"The Sense of Reality and Values of the Analyst as a Necessary Factor in Psychoanalysis," *The International Journal of Psychoanalysis,* Vol. 47 (1966), Part 4.

TABLE OF CONTENTS

I

THE FUNCTION OF HISTORY

———————————— ···━●◎●━··· ————————————

History and Biography

Psychiatry and psychoanalysis developed as an outgrowth of the discipline of medicine. One of the substantial benefits of this has been the inheritance of certain attitudes toward the collection of both historical and observational data. The point of view of the observer will inevitably influence what is observed and how it will be interpreted. However, a fuller appreciation of what he is looking for and what he wishes to accomplish will make him more useful and probably less biased as well.

In the study of the emotional disorders the emphasis in recent times has been upon the significance of the interview situation itself with a proportionate de-emphasis upon the collection of, and validation of, biographical data. This developed as a reaction against the pedestrian and unimaginative collection of "case histories" and the categorization of poorly conceptualized "disease states." Formerly there was a lack of grasp of the significance of the interview situation itself as the primary sphere of therapeutic interest and of data collection. However, one consequence of the more recent heavy emphasis upon the intra- and inter-personal experiences of the patient has been an unfortunate comparative neglect of the careful collection and reporting of biographical data and indeed of the data of observation themselves. There is, however, no intrinsic contradiction between these two points of view, and both of them are necessary for a well-conceived therapeutic approach to the emotional disorders.

In medicine the need to avoid biases of both a theoretical and personal nature was emphasized by Sydenham as early as the seventeenth century. He was the great exponent of the importance of careful description and recording of disease process, and with him a new era in medicine began. Thus, he states:

> In writing, therefore, a history of diseases, every philosophical hypothesis which hath prepossessed the writer in its favor ought to be totally laid aside, and then the manifest and natural phenomena of diseases, however minute, must be noted with the utmost accuracy; imitating in this the great exactness of painters, who, in their pictures, copy the smallest spots or moles in the originals. For 'tis difficult to give a detail of the numerous errors that spring from hypotheses, whilst writers, misled by false appearances, assign each phenomena for diseases, as never existed, but in their own brain; whereas they ought to appear clearly, if the truth of their favorite hypothesis, which they esteem incontestable were well established. Again, if any symptom properly suiting their hypothesis, does in reality belong to the disease they are about to describe, they lay too much stress upon it, as if nothing more was wanted to confirm it; whereas, on the contrary, if it does not agree with their hypothesis, their manner is, either to take no notice of it, or but barely to mention it, unless they can, by means of some philosophical subtlety, and adjust it thereto, and bring it in some measure to answer their end.[1]

As is not infrequently the case when something is misnamed, the error will cast its shadow over the thing itself. Deriving from its medical heritage, the individual biography, which is of such significance in understanding and treating human beings in emotional trouble, has come to be known as the "psychiatric history." But the word "history" is used in medicine in a quite different context. The term "history" came into use in medicine as a descriptive one for a disease process and was not referrable to the patient himself. While it is true that certain aspects of the patient's biography may be of importance even in a medical history, the central emphasis in medical "history taking" is upon the unearthing of the history of the disease or suspected disease process. Only on occasion does

[1] See the entire works of Dr. Thomas Sydenham (1634–89), trans. John Swan, M.D. (London, E. Cave at St. John's Gate, 1753), author's Preface 9(2):4–5.

the patient's biography become a subject of major importance in the usual medical history. For example, in exploring the causes of unexplained fever, the fact that the patient has been traveling in certain areas where exotic fevers are common may be a piece of highly relevant information.

As contrasted to medicine, in psychiatry the content of the patient's biography is central to the approach to him. Psychiatric disorders do not lend themselves to consideration as disease processes relatively divorced from the normal constitution and development of the individual. They are to be understood only in the context of the life history of the individual, and the personal biography becomes an essential facilitative device in the process of treatment.

The Need for Working Hypotheses

There are certain principles applicable to the collecting of biographical data which are relevant to all schools of dynamic psychiatric and psychoanalytic thought. While there is a tendency to emphasize differences rather than similarities between the various "schools" of psychiatric and psychoanalytic thought, including the so-called "eclectic" one, no one would gainsay the value of the careful, accurate, and organized collection of data which bear on the present reaction of the patient. In this regard there is no basic difference between the descriptive and dynamic approaches to psychiatry. A premature preoccupation with dynamic factors, without first collecting sufficient firm data, may lead to false conclusions. One of the most important skills in dealing with psychiatric patients is that of suspending judgment until the relevant facts are collected. It is most tempting to leap to conclusions based on biases and dislike of uncertainty. Just so, one of the most difficult problems in obtaining an adequate history is that of accepting deficits and unanswered questions in the available data. History is a series of discontinuous vignettes, and it is tempting to go beyond legitimate reconstructions and to manufacture a continuous, convincing picture. This latter may be unprovable or even full of rationalizations. The historian may employ overly rigid psychological theories as a mode of coping with his own intolerance for ambiguous and confusing data, and he may then fill the gaps and inadequacies in the history by elaborations of historical data based on his theory rather than on the available facts.

It is necessary, however, to have a theoretical system in order to organize historical data. It is a fallacy to assume that historical data can organize themselves. Those who entertain this fallacy are actually employing a theoretical system deriving from personal bias—a culturally imposed system, such as a "school" of psychiatric thought or sociologic thought or others—without being cognizant of it. In psychiatry the intent of the history and of the examination of the patient is to organize the biological trends of the individual, the internal factors, and the external environmental impact as represented by family and culture, into as plausible a picture as the data will permit. The intent of such organization in psychiatry is to come to some better appreciation of who this person is, what his modes of thinking and feeling are, why he behaves as he does, how he interacts with others, and what caused the present disorder. In another discipline, such as social relations, the intent for which data are being collected is different and hence the theory will differ accordingly.

The collection of historical data is intended to further the understanding of a present disorder. It is based on the premise that the patient can be understood in the context of time and space and that present dysfunction can best be understood as a continuity extending into the past. While this principle would seem to be quite elementary, the failure to appreciate it has for many translated the taking of a history into a dull, pedestrian, and boring duty; into an onerous side-activity intruding upon the main business of learning "to do therapy." However, the collection of historical data is a necessary and intrinsic part of the therapeutic process insofar as it is an instrument leading to greater understanding of the patient, his problems, and his conflicts. The therapeutic process is, in part, an unfolding of the history of the patient and itself becomes a part of the history of the patient of no small relevance.

The emphasis upon the history is not intended to overweigh the significance of the presenting symptoms. There has been a tendency to do this on the grounds that they are simply the "superficial" manifestations of "deeper" and more significant problems. However confusing and difficult to understand they may be, these symptoms

4

are nevertheless the expression of the drives and defenses in composite form. They must not be neglected in favor of abstract dynamics, just as the preoccupation with symptomatology alone should not lead to the neglect of dynamic clarifying concepts deriving from the past life of the patient.

History and the Therapeutic Process

No sharp line of distinction can be drawn between the taking of the history and the therapeutic process. The unfolding of the circumstances leading up to the present disorder, with the help of a skilled, impartial, and sympathetic person, offers opportunities for the beginning organization of new perspectives and new modes of coping with old repetitive and inadequate ways of dealing with problems. While empathic understanding and intuitive appreciation are crucial elements in the therapeutic process and indeed in the taking of the history itself, they are not substitutes for as disciplined an approach as possible to treatment itself.

History represents an organization of relevant, specific data about the patient as well as such reconstructions of prior events as will lend themselves to a meaningful picture of those events. It is intended to assist in clarifying present modes of thinking, feeling, and behaving on the patient's part. With this in mind, the mode of collecting data must be done with an eye to its potential impact on the therapeutic process. A structured sense of the general areas in which significant data might be obtained is essential on the part of the historian. This is particularly necessary since the data which are desired cannot be collected in a systematic fashion from the patient, and if the historian lacks an overview he may become lost in a welter of detail. While those who envision psychiatry in perhaps too rigid terms as a science might well err by a cold and unempathic collecting of "facts" in obtaining a history, those who envision psychiatry in the context of an "artistic" pursuit will tend to err in the opposite direction. It is a common fallacy to assume that the arts are only matters of sensual pursuit, since even the fine arts themselves are little but chaos without an underlying body of disciplined and technical considerations.

As has been mentioned, the careful collecting of historical data and the later revision of them unfortunately have been envisioned often as being antipathetic to the affective, emphatic, and intuitive modes of relating to the patient. This is false, since the biographical approach is the best way of gaining a "feel" for the patient and communicating this to him as well as eliciting a co-operative response from him. To listen to the patient's development of the circumstances out of which his present difficulties arose, to identify areas of special importance, and in general to share with him the areas in his developmental history that deserve special emphasis and exploration are crucial parts of treatment. The free-flowing attention to the unconscious activities of the patient is not hindered but is enhanced by this image of the historian's intelligence and technical skill.

Certain classes of reported data—as will be enlarged upon in the next chapter—are of doubtful accuracy. For instance, much of the data about child-rearing obtained from parents about their children, and particularly their grown children, are open to question as specific fact. Inquiry into these spheres does cast light, however, on their attitude toward the patient at least at this time, and in this sense at least the data collected are valuable. They are of little or no value as specified information, however.

Those aspects of the interview situation which have to do with the data of biography offer an unusually good opportunity to explore the ways in which the patient has conceptualized his world. If the interview is conducted with someone other than the patient—as sometimes becomes necessary in more severely disorganized states—it offers the opportunity to explore not only "facts" but prior interactions of the patient with this usually highly significant other person, be it a parent, sibling, or friend. When the patient is describing significant persons in his life, he is describing not only them but also attitudes toward himself and projections of his own inner life as well. The history offers numerous opportunities to observe the manner in which the informant conceptualizes his world. When the informant is not the patient, the patient's world is seen at second hand through the informant's eyes, and the informant's world—always significant in the patient's life—is seen at first hand.

Even a defensive image given by the patient or other informant may be revealing. A distorted or even false image tells something of the mode of relationship to the historian or even to the patient himself if the informant is some other person. Attitudes of a spouse toward his mate who is the patient are often revealed by the nature of his distortions as well as by his direct statements. Just so, the distortions of the parents of the schizophrenic may give valuable insights into the world in which the patient has lived. The patient himself inevitably distorts history, and therapy itself involves unraveling these distortions. Thus not only is the history itself important as a statement of facts, but it is also important as a record of the particular skewings and distortions that are a condition for the disorder that is brought for treatment.

That the patient and other informants report historical data from their own point of view is to be expected. Events are seen—and thus reported—dependent on their own biases. The informant will present a more positive or negative view of himself and others depending on his own characterological needs. It is the historian's task to avoid equivalent distortions and to retain his objectivity. He must tolerate the discomfort of dealing with incomplete and often fragmentary data. He must continue to explore and to enlarge on the available body of information in as objective a way as he can. The point of view of the observer can influence not only the interpretation of an event but also what is actually seen and heard, and the historian is capable of skewing events as well as is the patient. It is true, however, that the patient is reporting past events which were usually fraught with anxiety at the time of the event and are being retold to the historian in an often anxiety-laden situation. As a consequence, the patient is far more prone to have a biased view of events than is the historian. This is so, even aside from any technical skills, as such, which the historian as an expert may possess.

Intrinsic Versus Extrinsic Factors

It is difficult to strike a balance at any point in the conduct of a case between the attempts objectively to appraise the social experiences of the patient and the need to be cognizant of the world of his personal and inner experience—the world of needs, conflicts, and defenses. In general, the initial historical data tend to

7

be oriented more toward the social and interpersonal world of the patient, while the data obtained during the further development of the treatment process tend to be oriented more toward the world of inner experience. This is true, however, only in a relative sense, since in no circumstances is either frame of reference totally dominant.

Dynamic psychiatrists and psychoanalysts are primarily oriented toward the modes of manipulation of intrinsic problems, at least as their major sphere of operation. This is not to say that they devalue environmental factors, or even on occasion do not participate in environmental manipulations. This is certainly true when hospitalization is felt to be the treatment of choice. Their primary point of reference is nevertheless that of internal modes of functioning and the possibilities of change through alterations in them.

For purposes of illustration, one might compare the theoretical bias in dynamic psychiatry and psychoanalysis with that in the field of social relations. In the latter, the individual is seen as being subject to the influences of his environment. The environment is conceptualized as an orderly, predictable aggregate of persons, groups of persons, and things. These are subject to predictable characteristics and behavior and determine much, if not all, of what the newly emerging individual will be from cradle to grave. What his prejudice will be, with whom he will associate, whom he will marry, how he will vote, etc. are statistically predictable. In view of the environment's immense impact and capacity to influence the individual, there are those who are prone to reify the culture itself and to see it as a processing machine, essentially creating adult humans out of "raw material." This is a somewhat overdrawn image, but the emphasis on the enormous impact of folkways even on such matters as types of child rearing, etc., suggests that this is both a highly relevant frame of reference in its own right and has important although not primary significance in the psychiatric frame of reference as well.

While psychiatry can indeed learn much from the sociologist's view of man, it is not psychiatry's basic point of emphasis. In psychiatry the individual and his particular modes of adaptation or maladaptation based on intrinsic factors—however much they may have been developed in the context of earlier interpersonal and social factors—is primary. The goal of helping this particular individual is the heart of the matter, and the environmental situation is relevant only insofar as it casts light on the particular influence it may have brought to bear on the making of this unique person. The collection of historical data is done in an attempt to formulate just what influence such events have had upon present function and dysfunction. The individual in this sense is something more than a unit in the transmission of the culture; he is this as well as being a unique, alive, feeling being who has been subject to cultural influences which have broad similarities to those of others but who, because of his unique constitution and experiences, varies in significant ways from any other person. While it is untenable to study man as a product of his inborn drives alone, it is just as untenable to study him as an adult who is in one way or another catapulted into that estate without being partially formed by his own unique responses to his environment. Due cognizance must be given to inborn as well as environmental factors in psychiatry. The matter of the history of the development of the individual may be something less than absolutely validated from the rigidly scientific point of view, but it constitutes the best means for understanding and for coping with present disorders in the psychiatric context.

It is futile in clinical practice to become preoccupied with the question of which contributions to development and to the creation of a present disordered state are made by the inborn characteristics of the organism, and which are a result of postulated experiences with others. Needless to say, a theoretical system in psychiatry which summarily excludes one or the other of these will be biased. For example, if primary emphasis is placed upon the biological characteristics, such as the chemistry or physiology of brain function or the endocrine system, this becomes a separate microcosm, and behavior may be seen as secondary. In fact, behavior becomes a comparatively irrelevant side effect of these physiological events. So, in the reverse, overemphasis upon psychological drives or environmental factors may falsely place all other referents in a secondary and minor position.

While genetic as well as biochemical and neurophysiological events undoubtedly are significant factors in the emotional disorders, environmental events are of prime relevance in the practice of psychotherapy and psychoanalysis, and they are the meat of history. Even in manifest physical, bodily illnesses the role of the emotions and of the past history of the patient, in terms of his past life experiences, is of great importance. The tendency to separate even mental disorders into organic and functional states has made for a certain cloudiness of thinking and the obscuring of the tremendous interaction of these two frames of reference within any given patient whatever his primary diagnosis may be. For example, the earlier association of paresis with mania derived from undue preoccupation with the organic nature of this state. The assumption of specific emotional states based upon specific etiological agents and brain localizations invited the false view that a specific paretic behavioral pattern existed. As opposed to this, the modern view of the reaction pattern of the paretic is seen as a variable dependent on the patient's prior history and personality as well as upon the organic brain dysfunction.

In the development of the individual a continuous flow of experiences with persons who are themselves engaged in culturally determined roles takes place. These stimuli interact with the biologically and psychologically determined characteristics of the individual in order to produce the adult. It is the intent of the psychiatric history to set down a record of the forces from all of these sources. Within the limitations of the data available, this should represent a continuous related set of experiences from childhood to the present which offers a convincing image of the present state of affairs. Due emphasis is placed on the past state of affairs and the present situation of the patient insofar as they may contribute to present and anticipated disability. The areas in which the patient responds with a typical cultural response as well as those in which he does not are both relevant.

The Use of Language

The major means by which the history is usually obtained is through the use of words. In addition to words, there are other important communicative devices in the forms of gestures, intonation, etc., but words are the primary device. It is the task of the historian to identify communications offered in verbal or other forms and to make a meaningful *verbal*, formalized statement in the form of the individual history. This is no small task, and especially so since many words used for descriptive purposes in psychiatry are ambiguous and are often the source of major misunderstandings with patients and with colleagues as well.

A classic instance of the limitation of a descriptive term is the frequent unqualified use of the term depression. As Mendelson[2] has pointed out, the term depression is used for a potpourri of affective states. The span of these states extends from the depressed phase of manic-depressive psychosis to the existential states of isolation, emptiness, and loneliness. That the patient uses the term depression—in a non-technical sense—to mean one or another of these affective states is quite logical. It is the function of the historian, however, to explore with the patient the particular meaning that must be applied to this term for this unique person.

As will be elaborated upon later, language may be used for a variety of functions and may conceal as well as reveal information. Thus words are often used, particularly by the obsessional, in such a fashion that they are isolated from any accompanying feeling. He may speak with considerable fluency about what one might expect to be the most harrowing, difficult, and distressing situations as if he were simply a non-feeling reporter of events. It is often intriguing to observe that when his obsessional defenses crumble the same events will be described with a great deal more feeling but with proportionately less fluency. To further illustrate, the term "love" is sometimes used as if it represented a physical commodity. It is not uncommon for a mother, for instance, to talk of giving her child an hour of love when what she means is that she has spent an hour with her child. Love can be qualified as to its object and its intensity—it cannot be weighed on a scale like potatoes.

The Function of Treatment

Since present interpersonal conflicts are regularly expressive of prior conflicts, it would seem that an understanding of the patient's

---

[2] Myer Mendelson, *Psychoanalytic Concepts of Depression* (Springfield, Ill.; C. C Thomas, 1960), p. 170.

past would help to illuminate present conflicts. There are those who would argue that since present conflicts are in fact repetitive, recourse to considerations of the past are irrelevant. However, in view of the complexity of any given case, cues obtained from a careful consideration of the patient's past history could not fail to help.

Present modes of behavior are based on learned responses which derive from prior experiences. They are prone to be repetitive in nature, and a historical knowledge of the prior experiences in connection with which they were evolved can assist in making sense out of current behavior which is otherwise impossible to understand. Many essentially conditioned responses are intrinsic to each person's character structure. These include certain cue situations. For example, certain specific other persons are perceived or experienced in a stereotypical fashion based on prior relationships. In addition, there are automatic modes of response which are no longer dependent on any apparent external stimulus. In the actual taking of a history, the tendency of the patient or other informant to structure the interview situation itself and to see the person of the historian himself in the context of prior experience is representative of this phenomenon. The informant will respond intellectually and emotionally to the historian as he is perceived by him and not according to the historian's self-image. Awareness of this will often make sense out of otherwise senseless performances.

The function of collecting historical data in therapeutic work is, in the final analysis, one of influencing events in the present and in the future. One of the potential dangers of becoming concerned with historical events is that one may become so preoccupied with them that the collection of such information may become an end in itself. If this occurs, it will defeat the therapeutic purpose. However much events of the past may be validated, and however much they may have been inevitable consequences of circumstances existing in the past, they are examined with the intent of opening up new possibilities for coping with the present and the future.

The intent of the exploration of the past is to define repetitive and maladaptive ways of functioning. The purpose of this is not only to clarify why the present state of affairs exists but to establish, through it, new possibilities for dealing with the present and the future in a different way. The dilemma in the emotional disorder

12

is that the patient is entrapped in the past and cannot envision any other state of affairs. If he is invited to explore the past he will often do so and then cast blame on those whom he finds blameworthy—such as his parents—as if he could, by so doing, force them to change the present and the future. Alternatively, if he is invited to explore his own participation in past events, he may engage in a veritable bath of guilt as if this could do any more than concretize equivalent behavior and experience in the present and the future.

The function of the therapeutic process is to resolve this tension between the past and the present and future. For the patient to blame his parents or himself for past events is in the end a futile process. There are phases in treatment where we must indeed recognize and experience fully that such blame does indeed exist when it has previously been out of awareness. In the end, however, he must come to know that his hate and guilt have a paralyzing influence on his potential capacity to reshape his present and his future. The intent of the historian is not simply to assign cause and responsibility for events in the past but also to place them in a perspective which invites action in the present and the future. The intent is fully to accept present responsibility and freedom to choose.

The way the past is seen is determined by present needs. During the course of therapy the patient's remembered version of past events often changes markedly. Thus not only is it valid to say that the past influences the present, but also that the memory of the past is modified, at least, by present experience. Finally, both present experiences and remembered experiences from the past greatly influence the present and the future.

II

THE PHILOSOPHY OF HISTORY

——————————— ...◗◉◖... ———————————

History and the Case History

Many of the issues which are considered in this book have been of major concern to philosophers of history of various persuasions. It is a useful working hypothesis to assume that historical events have some degree of orderliness and are not simply a meaningless jumble of unrelated happenings. Based on this proposition is the premise that cause-and-effect relationships are potentially discoverable in connection with successive events. The assumption is made that there is a design in nature, and while it is not always demonstrable, that events involving humans can be approached with the intent of establishing the patterns underlying them just as physical events of other kinds can be studied in this fashion. Superficially, this might appear to be a self-evident proposition. It has, however—despite its advantages—been the source of much confusion and misinformation. This derives from the fact that in human affairs the possibilities of the interpretation of events in the context of preconceived ideas and hypotheses is infinite. Even the data which are collected by a skilled investigator at first-hand are subject to his point of view, bias, and prejudices. To the degree to which he has a particular system of values and an aim in examining historical data it will affect and significantly determine the very nature of the information obtained. His motivations in examining human affairs, both intellectual and personal, will become a part of the data itself, and the use which he wishes to make of the information obtained will inevitably introduce biases into the selection of certain facts themselves from the total mass of information available about any human event.

From the sixteenth century on, history has been conceptualized as having inherent evolutionary tendencies, and the fruits of this approach have enhanced the view that history obeys logical laws. An illustration of the imposition of a particular point of view on human events is the Marxist philosophy of history. It premises that the very existence and character of man are dictated by historical forces and that there is a historical inevitability controlling him. Like many other propositions of its kind it has a measure of attractiveness, and no doubt a measure of truth. Its global quality excludes, however, many other equally attractive views of the impact of history on man as a biological organism.

An example of a very different approach to history is that which rejects the rational and linear view of history with its universal structure, and which is based on a deterministic and teleological philosophy. It takes the position that history is an academic discipline subject to the rigid rules of science. It invites attention to the detailed and careful examination of specific historical events and the greatest conservatism in the interpretation of events and the linking of successive events. There is a de-emphasis of the "grand design." As will be developed, this apparently simplistic view has given rise to some intriguing paradoxes.

It is evident that there is a close parallel between the problems relevant to the study of history in general and those having to do with the study of the biography of the individual. The latter are of central concern in psychiatry and psychoanalysis. Thus, one can see the spectrum of theories of history in operation through the study of the various schools of thought among psychiatric practitioners. These extend all the way from rigidly preformed and strongly teleological systems, in the light of which biographical events are seen and interpreted, to extremely loosely structured examinations of specific events, including those of the present or recent past. There may be even a studied rejection of any attempt at the linkage of apparently related events and a total rejection of any overview of biographical events. In view of the parallelism between the philosophy of history and the philosophy of the particular kind of biography which is used in psychiatry and psychoanalysis, a brief presentation of some critical conflicting views in the field of the philosophy of history will add perspective. In so doing there will be no pretension of a comprehensive survey. Instead, representative samples will be offered to illustrate different points of view. The intent is not to establish that the philosophy of history is entirely analogous but to invite the reader to approach the subject matter of individual biography with some freedom from the usual stereotypes.

History as "Science"

Although seemingly paradoxical, the modern scientific approach to history and the reaction against it can be observed in the theories advanced by a single man—Leopold von Ranke. He was torn between historicism—or Universal History—and the wish to establish history as a positive science. Historicism is representative of the romantic approach to history. It postulates that history has to do with human life in all of its complexity. It takes a wholistic view of the human situation including not only the documents of history but the life and customs of the people as well. As opposed to this, his desire to approach history as an exact science prompted Ranke to develop the proposition that each event deserves study as a discrete entity. From this viewpoint, it is related to other events but is a thing unto itself. The particular event is to be eventually understood in the context of the over-all plan which would emerge from the approximation of a sufficient number of such discrete events. Using Ranke's contradiction as a point of departure, developments occurred in two opposing directions. Ranke developed the "scientific approach" with its strengths and limitations; others have proceeded in a quite different direction. There is a clear parallel in the careful, descriptive, Kraepelinian approach to psychiatric history and the psychodynamic approach.

Based on the proposition that there are no a priori universals in history, Ranke proceeded to address himself to the particular in history with the long view of developing generalizing principles from these particulars. In effect, he invoked the deductive position of modern science. By means of the careful exploration of documents, the use of archeological findings, etc., and the development of techniques for appraising the validity of the data collected, a substantial body of validated "facts" was collected from which general propositions could hopefully then be made. The consequence of this was the development of new and careful techniques for the examination and documentation of events, and in this connection the development of a badly needed systematic and careful approach to the data of history. While there was the promise that out of such a systematization general and universal principles of history would evolve, this was not realized, and scholars tended to become mired down in the study of details. Generalizing principles were sparse and narrow in scope.

A Relativistic View of History

In reaction against the limitations imposed by this "scientific" approach to history, there were those—among whom Freud can be numbered—who saw man as being governed by irrational forces both in the individual and in the collective, and who saw the rational, scientific approach to human events as being the façade behind which the true course of events in all of its irrationality was being enacted. By irrationality it was not suggested that there was no underlying pattern of events, but rather that the manifest pattern was a justification for unconscious and highly motivated universal patterns deriving eventually from the biological needs of man. Thus certain general patterns of family structure and of family interaction as an organic unit of which the individual was a part were defined. The individual both interacted with the family and made it a part of himself. This was then offered as the explanation for all sorts of human experience and behavior.

Such insights into psychological dynamics inevitably invited the examination of the participation of the historian himself in the version of history offered, insofar as he is the interpreter of the historical event. Let us look at one facet of the problem. When is the historian entitled to have opinions as to the motivations of the creator of an historical document? What data and what system of psychology shall he use in coming to his conclusions as to motivations? The question of where his opinion rests on science, where on art, and where on the intuitive empathic sense of the interpreter takes one into areas only too familiar to the psychiatrist and psycho- analyst. As opposed to exponents of historicism, those who espouse the relativistic view place great emphasis upon the attitudes and character of the historian himself as a crucial factor in the interpreta- tion of history. Here the psychiatrist and psychoanalyst are indeed on familiar grounds! The remainder of this chapter will concentrate upon this area of special interest and importance.

Past and Present

Emphasis upon the interlocking nature of past and present events has become an increasing tide in historical scholarship. If either of them is to be understood, both must be understood. The intermeshed nature of past and present has been stressed by Frederick Jackson Turner,[1] among others. He emphasized the developing nature of history and the impact of the present point of view on past events and the reverse. Thus:

> History, both objective and subjective is ever *becoming*, never completed. The centuries unfold more and more the meaning of past times. Today we understand Roman history better than did Livy or Tacitus, not only because we know how to use the sources better but also because the significance of events develops with time, because today is so much a product of yesterday that yesterday can only be understood as it is ex- plained by today. The aim of history, then, is to know the elements of the present by understanding what came into the present from the past. For the present is simply the developing past, the past the undeveloped present. As well try to under- stand the egg without a knowledge of its developed form, the chick, as to try to understand the past without bringing to it the explanation of the present: and equally well try to under- stand an animal without study of its embryology as to try to understand one time without study of the events that went before. The antiquarian strives to bring back the past for the

---

[1] Frederick Jackson Turner, 1861–1932. "The Significance of History," in *The Early Writings of Frederick Jackson Turner* (Madison, Wisc.: Univer- sity of Wisconsin Press, 1938).

sake of the past: the historian strives to show the present to itself by revealing its origin from the past. The goal of the antiquarian is the dead past: the goal of the historian is the living present. Droysen has put this true conception into the statement, "History is the KNOW THYSELF of humanity—the self-consciousness of mankind."

The Creative Imagination of the Historian

It is a short step from the position espoused by Turner to the proposition that history must include the creative imagination of the historian. The inclusion of the historian as the person doing the "understanding" introduces the need to examine his normal biases. The "know thyself" of the historian represents a parameter that has only come under examination fully in this century. It parallels and merges with the strong emphasis by the psychoanalyst on the rule that he examine his own needs and biases insofar as they affect his perception of the patient and the historical development of present malfunction.

Since a given historical event rests upon a substrate of things which actually transpired at some point in the past, it always has a basis in external reality or actuality. The problem with any reported historical event is that of how to separate the actual event from its interpretation by the historian, and this is possible within limits. There is a difference between poor and good historical scholarship as well as poor and good historians. Propaganda distorts history for its purposes and is not the same as careful and scholarly examinations of past events. As might be expected, various historians have taken opposing views about the relative objectivity of history. The following statement by Morton White[2] is representative of those who argue for the objectivity of history as against the skepticism of historical relativism:

. . . The mere fact that historians are biased is no argument against the existence of impersonal standards, and it seems absurd to argue from their limitations to standards which would justify their limitations. It has been argued fallaciously

[2] Morton White, "Can history be objective?" in Social Thought in America (New York: Viking Press, 1949).

19

that because of the admitted existence of value-dominated selection we must recognize that it is part of the accredited procedure of history. However, it is important to remember that
this hurried flight to relativism starts with recognizing that the
whole truth is the aim of the historian. And since he cannot attain his ideal, since he cannot record all the true statements,
he is advised by relativists to pick out those which accord
with his scheme of reference, his interests and his problems.
In short, he is advised to pay no attention to his unattainable
idea; he is advised to forget about it. But this is a non sequitur.
Since we cannot present the whole truth we are fallaciously
advised to select those truths which interest us. But the net
effect of this is not to help the historian approximate his admitted ideal. How can he approximate it if he forswears the
task of approximating it and turns to selection guided by his
values and prejudices?

White justifiably fears that a surrender to complete skepticism
would make for sloppy scholarship and be used as an excuse to
avoid the laborious task of unraveling, within possible limits, the
actuality of events. There are events "out there" which have an
objective character if they can be disentangled from the biases,
prejudices, and valuative judgments of the observer, and this is
a useful ideal even though it can never be entirely attained. There
are some intriguing parallels in present-day psychiatry and psychoanalysis in which a highly relativistic view of history is the vogue.
The emphasis on the interview situation and the de-emphasis upon
careful history-taking has the advantage of stressing the importance of
the two-person, patient-therapist relationship as the central therapeutic lever. It has been used by many, however, as an excuse for the
sloppy organization of historical data. One of the consequences of
this is that theories are derived from reports of introspective experiences bearing little relationship to actual past events. This
is frequently overlooked, and theories are constructed based upon
these introspective reports as if the stated events had actually occurred as described. Such false theories of human development
are then used, in a circular fashion, to "clarify" the meaning of
introspective historical reports of whole masses of patients. This
stands in sharp contradistinction to longitudinal studies of actual
child development and the ensuing theories based on these actual
observations.

The Middleground

A more conservative view of historical relativism has been advanced by W. H. Walsh,[3] and this represents the position making for the optimal use of history by psychiatrists and psychoanalysts.

The suggestion I am making is that historians approach the past each with his own philosophical ideas, and that this has a decisive effect on the way they interpret it. If I am right, differences between historians are in the last resort differences of philosophies, and whether we can resolve them depends on whether we can resolve philosophical conflicts. But I can well imagine that these assertions will involve some strain on the reader's credulity. "Are you seriously suggesting," I shall be asked, "that *all* historians impart moral and metaphysical prejudices into their work, thus as it were contemplating the past through spectacles which cannot be removed? And if you are, are you not confusing what is true of history at a crude and unscientific level only with what is true of all history?" No doubt ethical, religious or, if you like, metaphysical prejudices can be shown to mar popular historical works of all kinds; but can the same be said of the writings of reputable historians? Is it not apparent that historical thinking can be effective only so far as the historian forgets the ethical, religious and metaphysical outlook of his own age and tries to see his facts in the way those he was writing of did? Must he not read the past in terms, not of his own conception of what human nature is or ought to be, but in terms of the ideas held by those who were alive at the time he is studying? And do we not differentiate good and bad work in history by examining how far particular writers have done just this—by seeing how far they have freed themselves from their preconceptions and contrived to put themselves in the places of the person whose actions they are recounting?

There is obviously much sense in this criticism, yet I doubt even so if it is wholly effective. Certainly there is a difference of the kind indicated between good and bad work in history, a difference we bring out by describing the former as "authentic" and the latter as "unimaginative." Exercising the imagination is an important part of historical thinking, and it does consist

[3] W. H. Walsh, *Philosophy of History: an Introduction* (New York: Harper and Brothers, 1958).

in trying, so far as we can, to put ourselves in the places of those whose actions we are studying. But, as we saw before, there are very real difficulties in holding that putting oneself in another man's place is a simple intuitive process: it seems rather to depend on the accumulated experience of the person who carries it out. And when we speak of "experience" here I think we must recognize that this too is not a simple term. My understanding of the ancient world depends on what I have myself experienced or assimilated from the experience of others; but, as was pointed out, there seems to be in all such experiences a subjective or a priori element contributed by myself. When I try to put myself in the place of an ancient Greek or a medieval cleric or a Victorian parent, in order to write the history of the ancient world or the medieval church or the Victorian family, I must certainly put aside, so far as I can, the moral and metaphysical preconceptions of my own time. But I cannot escape, if I am to make any sense of my material, making some general judgments about human nature, and in these I shall find my own views constantly cropping up. I shall find myself involuntarily shocked by this event and pleased by that, unconsciously seeing this action as reasonable and that as the reverse. And however much I tell myself to eschew my own prejudices and concentrate on understanding what actually happened, I shall not succed in carrying out the injunction to the letter, since understanding itself is not a passive process but involves the judging of evidence by principles whose truth is independently assumed.

Facts and Meaning

Attention will now be directed towards the differentiation between the "facts" of history and the meaning and significance which we place upon those facts. What we know as an historical fact is a generalization of a whole mass of data. Thus, for example, let us suppose that a patient states that he was married in 1950. This statement of "fact" includes an endless series of other "facts" of a greater or lesser degree of relevance to the task at hand. In truth, if an attempt were made to spell out in its totality all of the historical data surrounding the initial "fact," one would end up with a weighty tome. The truth is that we select certain particularly relevant events associated with the initial event which have especial meaning and significance and make generalizations based on these which are relevant to the particular use we wish to make of them. In therapy that particular use is to help patients develop new, more useful, and happier modes of coping. The fact of marriage in 1950 has little relevance as an event isolated from all other related occurrences. It is being reported by the patient, not simply as a statistical event, but as part of a complex web of circumstances extending before and beyond it that has a greater or lesser bearing on the circumstances for which he now comes seeking help. Thus the initial fact has many ramifications and is not a thing unto itself with sharp and clear outlines. It constitutes a symbol which is representative of a mass of related historical data.

Carl Becker,[4] an exponent of this point of view, poses three questions about the historical fact: the *what, where,* and *when* of it. To the *what* he states:

> . . . [the historian] cannot deal directly with the event itself, since the event itself has disappeared. What he can deal with directly is a *statement about the event.* He deals in short not with the event, but with a statement which affirms *the fact that the event occurred.* When we really get down to the hard facts, what the historian is always dealing with is an *affirmation*—an affirmation of the fact that something is true. There is thus a distinction of capital importance to be made: the distinction between the ephemeral event which disappears, and the affirmation about the event which persists. For all practical purposes it is this affirmation about the event that constitutes for us the historical fact. If so the historical fact is not the past event, but a symbol which enables us to recreate it imaginatively. Of a symbol it is hardly worthwhile to say that it is cold or hard. It is dangerous to say even that it is true or false. The safest thing to say about a symbol is that it is more or less appropriate.

As to the *where* of a historical fact, Becker places it in someone's mind and insists that an historical fact *is*—not *was.* The fact as history is a matter of the present—the historical event is not transpiring now. While the actual past event is gone forever it is remembered, and it is the persistence of records and memories rather

⁴ Carl L. Becker, "What Are Historical Facts?" *Western Political Quarterly* 8(3), 1955.

than the ephemeral event that makes a difference to us now. In therapy, both conscious and unconscious memories are relevant insofar as they derive from historical contexts. He next addresses himself to *what* is a historical fact as follows: "If the historical fact is present, imaginatively, in someone's mind, then it is now a part of the present." The present moment is evanescent and hence even in exploring a historical event we are engaged in a complex of time present, time past, and time to come.

With the development of the social sciences, scientific methodology and statistical techniques were applied to historical material with illuminating results. They could not replace the methods of history but added a new dimension, just as research in the behavioral sciences is not a substitute for methods previously employed for personality study but has been the source of new outlooks in therapy.

The Social Scientist and History

Hofstadter's[5] description of the social scientist's potential contribution to the historian might as well have been a description of the social scientist's value to the therapist. He states:

> But to me it is not the formal methods of the social sciences, useful as they may be, that are of central significance, but rather their substantive findings, their intellectual concerns, and their professional perspectives. Taken in this way, their value paradoxically rests not in their ability to bring new methods to bear upon old problems but in their ability to open new problems which the historian has usually ignored. Prompted by the social sciences, the historian begins to realize that matters of central concern to other disciplines force him to enlarge his conception of his task. Questions associated with social status, social mobility, differences and conflicts between generations, child-rearing in its relation to culture, the sociology of knowledge and of the professions, are questions which he might properly take upon himself, and which are interwoven with his traditional concerns . . .

[5] Richard Hofstadter, "History and the Social Sciences," in *The Varieties of History*, ed. Fritz Stern (New York: Meridian Books, 1956).

And a bit later:

> . . . the fundamental value of these perspectives is in their addition to the speculative richness of history. The more the historian learns from the social sciences, the more variables he is likely to take account of, the more complex his task becomes. The results may be that his conclusions become more tenuous and tentative, but this is a result to be welcomed. The closer the historian comes, with whatever aids, to the full texture of historical reality, the more deeply is he engulfed in a complex web of relationships which he can hope to understand only in a limited and partial way. . . .

The application of the techniques of the behavioral sciences to the study of biography—of the case history—has added considerably to our perspective. Thus, as discussed elsewhere in this book, the comparison of verified historical events in children's lives and the memories of their mothers throws illuminating insights on the patterning of recalled data and of reconstructions. Studies of patterns of response in various socio-economic groups, linguistics, group responses to propaganda, etc., have changed the psychiatrist's expectations and mode of looking at and interpreting the data of even the individual history itself, although that history has a unique and special quality for each patient.

Will and Determinism

The final issue to be considered here bearing on the subject of the philosophy of history is the eternal one of determinism versus free will, a subject long familiar to the field of psychiatry. Isaiah Berlin[6] has written fluently in this area and defines the role of free will and determinism in human affairs in a useful way. He points out the limitation of the concept of determinism as follows:

> My submission is that to make a serious attempt to adapt our thoughts and words to the hypothesis of determinism is scarcely feasible, as things are now, and have been within recorded history. The changes involved are too radical: our moral cate-

[6] Isaiah Berlin, *Historical Inevitability* (New York: Oxford University Press, 1954).

gories are, in the end, not much more flexible than our physical ones: we cannot begin to think out in real terms, to which behavior and speech would correspond, what the universe of the genuine determinist would be like, any more than we can think out, with the minimum of indispensable concrete detail (i.e., begin to imagine) what it would be like to be in a timeless world, or one with a seventeen-dimensional space. Let those who doubt this try for themselves; the symbols with which we think will hardly lend themselves to the experiment; they, in their turn, are too deeply involved in our normal view of the world, allowing for every difference of period and clime and culture, to be capable of so violent a break . . . Hence the ancient controversy between will and determinism, while it remains a genuine issue for theologians and philosophers, need not trouble the thoughts of those whose concern is with empirical matters—the actual lives of humans in the space and time of normal experience. For historians determinism is not a serious issue.

Berlin does then find some virtue in the deterministic hypothesis:

The irrelevance of this general hypothesis to historical studies must not blind us to its importance as a specific corrective to ignorance, prejudice, dogmatism, and fantasy on the part of those who judge the behavior of others. For it is plainly a good thing that we should be reminded by social scientists that the scope of human choice is a good deal more limited than we used to suppose; that the evidence at our disposal shows that many of the acts too often assumed to be within the individual's control are not so; that man is an object in nature to a larger degree than has at times been supposed, that human beings more often than not act as they do because of characteristics due to heredity or physical or social environment or education, or biological laws or physical characteristics or the interplay of these factors with each other, and with the obscurer factors loosely called physical characteristics; and that the resultant habits of thought, feeling, and expression are as capable of being classified and made subject to hypotheses and systematic predictions as the behavior of material objects.

The issue of determinism has continued to be of concern in psychiatry and psychoanalysis. With their commitment to science, they tend toward a deterministic position in the more abstract and theoretical frame of reference. When an actual patient is being considered, however, heavy emphasis is placed on free will and on his capacity to sway the course of events through his own decisions. Berlin's position offers latitude for this dual orientation in a useful way.

The close parallel between the issues involved in the philosophy of history and in the philosophy of the particular sort of biography employed in psychiatric treatment are inescapable. Useful working hypotheses are all that we can anticipate in both, but this is a very great deal at that. As is true in many disparate fields, the kinds of problems which are to be dealt with and the potential solutions available often have a great deal in common. Only too frequently scholars in fields sharing common interests are insulated from each other by mutual ignorance and prejudice, and areas where they might be of use to each other are ignored. While not germane to the present considerations, the historian, engrossed in the study of the motivations of historical figures, often rejects in wholesale fashion the available hypotheses about human behavior which are the everyday business of psychiatry and psychoanalysis.

III

THE MEANING OF HISTORY

The Relativity of History

The therapeutic process is an interaction in the present, conceptually bound to the historical past of the patient. If the patient and his problems are to be understood history is to be understood, and yet there is little general interest in the broad topic of history throughout the field of personality study. There is a universal tendency to assume that history refers to matters that had existence only in the past. As discussed in the last chapter, many historians have emphasized that history is always a matter of the present; only the subject-matter—the actual event—is of the past. In this chapter, the function of the examination of the past in terms of its usefulness to us in the present will be explored. Of course in the context of our immediate interest this will be in the specific area of personality study and of treatment.

The need for historical data in the examination and treatment of psychiatric patients is universally accepted. As is often the case with such an obvious process, the nature, credibility, and function of such data have been little considered with a view to specifying the underlying assumptions involved. Dynamic psychiatry has generally placed great emphasis on the importance of prior life experiences as causal factors in the emotional disorders. The major source of such data is the patient himself; data are sometimes available from relatives or other significant persons, and some information may be supplied from such sources as old diaries, etc. With all this, the primary if not the only source of significant historical experiences is the memory of such events on the part of the patient himself.

Empirical experience shows that an approach along historical lines tends toward a loosening up of fixed patterns of response constituting emotional disorders of one kind or another with the resultant opportunity to establish more gratifying modes of behavior for the particular individual. Something of a gradient exists among the various psychotherapies as regards the degree of dependence upon such reconstructions of past history, with orthodox psychoanalysis taking the position that a genetic reconstruction based on a convincing recall of early life experiences is a necessary condition for substantial change. The various deviant psychoanalytic groups and the dynamic psychotherapies place a decreasing emphasis upon such reconstructions of prior events, but, for the most part, some degree of emphasis on such memories is considered to be a matter of significance in all groups. In accord with this, dependent on their particular theoretical framework, each group tends to find significance in different reported prior events or to find different meaning in the same event. Thus an inevitable and necessary selection and ordering of the facts occurs. It need hardly be said that each group is inclined—as humans are prone to do—to feel that their way and their way alone is the way of truth and understanding.

There are several classes of reported, recalled events during the course of the treatment process, with, of course, gradients between them. Thus there are, first, the freely remembered and reported incidents of prior experience. Second, there are those incidents which are revealed only gradually but which the patient claims did not seem significant or which he did not reveal for other reasons. Finally, there are those memories which the patient claims to have forgotten, and to which he may even respond with some surprise at their recovery in treatment but which have a convincing sense of familiarity to him when recalled. Intermingled with the strict matter of the recall of past events are the interpretations which the patient has heretofore placed on such events. This includes the significance which the patient may place on the forgotten and now remembered event, as well as the tendency on his part to emphasize one or another aspect of prior experience. Paralleling this series of interpretations on the patient's part are the interpretations on the part of the therapist of the meaning of such events which are reported to him. His interpretations may or may not coincide with the patient's interpretation of the same reported events. It is usually the therapist's opinion that if a 'true' interpretation of the recalled events is arrived at in the context of the transference relationship, this will serve to correct aberrations of behavior.

Even within any one given frame of reference, any specific remembered event may be interpreted in different fashions at different points in therapy. This is said to stem from the need to adjust the interpretation to "where the patient is," to his degree of resistance, to the "level" he is presently working on, etc. To illustrate, the memory of a separation experience from a loved object with the resultant feelings of grief, depression, and impotence may be interpreted on different occasions as being due to oral deprivation, or as being a castration experience, or some other loss, dependent on the therapist's appraisal of the more significant theme at the moment. Of course, within a different theoretical framework, the phenomenon of separation itself may be used as the basic dynamic, or in yet another, the actual interaction involved in the reporting of the past event to the therapist as an event involving therapist and patient may be designated as the fundamental event. Notice that the emphasis here is on what is considered as bedrock. Many systems place importance on a number of different aspects of the reported event, but each tends to choose certain ones of them or even a single aspect as being of a primary order of importance in psychological development and in the therapeutic process.

Putting aside any manifest naïveté, resistance, or countertransference phenomena, the therapeutic task necessarily involves the values of the examiner. In exploring any event with the patient— even a present event much less a past one—all the possible facts about it cannot be included. At best the data felt to be relevant to a particular task are culled from the total body of information available. The facts do not impose a meaning on themselves; he who examines them assigns meaning to them and makes certain tacit assumptions in the process. The adequacy of the explanation of a given chain of events cannot be divorced from what we wish to do with the explanation. How fully and how far back toward original causes one wishes to seek is a question of utility, since in the true sense there is no end point. In the same sense, the choice of the specific events which are said to be causal posits that other concurrent events are not significant within that context. This may or may not be the case, but it is a necessary and logical assumption.

In psychiatry and psychoanalysis the utilitarian goal is that of helping other humans in distress. As a result, the search for historical events as remembered by the patient is directed toward the goal of alleviating such distress. The therapist's eventual purpose is to attain certain therapeutic goals, and his interest in history—as history—presumes that, if the genetic causes of the present state are revealed, then, and only then, can the present state of distress be fully alleviated. While there have been ample cautions offered through the years against the therapist's neurotic preoccupation with bringing about change in his patients, this is not intended to exclude the task of the therapist as a potentially helpful person. In most therapeutic approaches, the reconstruction of a plausible life history is considered a *sine qua non* for effective therapy. A widespread further assumption is that *plausibility* is equivalent to a validated history; that consensus between patient and therapist means that the stated historical events are proven facts even though the sole source of data may be the memory of the patient.

Is the Plausibility of History Enough?

Putting aside the matter of the therapeutic usefulness of this approach, if the matter of plausibility is unacceptable as validation, what might be accepted as such? After all, such matters as the date of birth, date of marriage, etc., are historical events which can be documented. In addition, reported incidents may sometimes be validated through other observers, and this is in fact one of the best means of validation. Although specific data may be distorted for defensive reasons, if this can be overcome there are precise means of documentation.

A typical example of an historical incident which was distorted for defensive reasons and which could be unravelled definitely is the following.

For some months during the course of treatment a patient reported that his mother had had two episodes of coronary thrombosis with the usual accompanying periods of hospitalization. Although his professional training was such as to have permitted access to her medical history, he had regularly rejected seeking any definitive information and, in fact, warded off the opportunity when medical data about her were offered gratuitously. Finally, such corroboration was sought by the patient, and it was established that the mother, in fact, never had had a coronary occlusion. The two periods of alleged hospital admissions had been periods of stay in the recovery room in the out-patient department of a hospital.

The reasons for the defensive operation are superfluous in the present connection, but the source from which the defense was created was the following. The mother had described these episodes as "heart attacks" and said that she was "hospitalized." The patient, for unconscious reasons of his own and despite his professional knowledge, translated "heart attack" into coronary occlusion and then added the period of hospitalization consistent with this diagnosis. I may add that the cue to the discovery of his distortion of history was the warding off of the discussion of the issue of her illness when he was approached by her physician.

Finally, some types of material can be validated by implication. For instance, when one is given a sufficient series of reported memories, the intervening events can with some authority be presumed to have occurred. As an example, we can assume if the patient reports that he lived in city *A* at age four and in city *B* at age six, that his family must have moved in the interim, although this is not a remembered event.

The dilemma arises when preconceived notions are substituted for legitimate linkages. The assumption that the reported memories are more than is apparent on the surface but are also symbolic images such as condensations, displacements, and distortions of whole masses of events is necessary. This can be used as license, however, for positing linkages of the most elaborate sort on the flimsiest of evidence. Even in such instances, however, insofar as the therapist and patient may share a convincing sense of the actuality of the alleged events, it may be therapeutic in its effect. While the therapist very legitimately chooses to use certain general hypotheses, extreme care is necessary to ascertain what the patient actually *did* experience and not what he *could* have experienced. The latter meets the criteria of the possible but may have no relevance to the particular patient. Thus there can be certain useful general guiding principles in exploring the structuring of the personality, but there can be no ultimate secret of personality development since each human has a unique constellation of experiences and of memories.

Even data obtained from independent observers cannot be accepted simply at face value since conflicting versions of the same event are not infrequent. An illustration of this will help to clarify this issue: in adult life, a sister and brother compare their memories of a past event.

Sister's version: "When we were younger, you were mother's favorite. You used to bring home chocolate eclairs and give them to her."

Brother's version: "No, that is not entirely correct. As I remember it, I would, in fact, give them to mother, and she would say, 'Thank you, son. Your little brother *loves* chocolate eclairs.'"

Both siblings experienced the remembered "eclair event" as being painful, each one gives a plausible version, and the two versions are parallel to a degree. The difference between them is very great, however. Each suggests some type of disruption in the relationship to mother, but this does not make them descriptively alike. In exploring the difficulties in validating this particular, relatively simple historical event, one can gain some sense of the difficulties in validating even more complex events. Further, even an actual comparing of notes between the siblings has not served to alter their individual views of what actually did transpire.

As regards the specific matter of therapy, the memory of the above event as reported by one or the other of the siblings would, along with many other such memories, be constructed into a mutually agreed-upon and plausible enough image of past events. This would take on meaning as a cause of present disability. As it happened, both siblings remembered the event in specific yet different contexts and interpreted it as connoting discrimination against themselves and favoritism for another, accompanied by guilt for having such feelings. Each of them, however, placed differing emphasis on the characters involved. It remains an open question as to whether it would significantly influence the course in therapy of either the brother or sister if it could never be established what mother did with the eclair. This simple incident is repeated a thousand times over and is the stuff from which history is created. In the process of therapy the patient and therapist jointly participate in the remaking of history insofar as it has been heretofore envisioned by the patient. Much of what is considered insight is the remaking of the historical past from the new perspectives available in the therapeutic situation. This new view of the historical past may claim some closer resemblance to the 'actual facts' as revealed by the lifting of repressions, but it may lay a far greater claim to the revealing of heretofore unavailable perspectives.

To what extent is the modification of emotionally laden memories in themselves the therapeutic factor, whether or not there is actual coincidence with actual past persons or events? It is evident that some degree of correspondence must occur, and it is possible that the therapist's logical as well as intuitive and empathic corresponding image bears a specific resemblance to the actual person and the actual past event being described. The fact is that the actual proof of such coincidence is not insisted upon in the conduct of therapy. The evident assumption is that this is a matter of the second order of importance. Emphasis is placed upon the fact that a consensus is arrived at with the patient and that certain commonly agreed-upon prior experiences which appeal to a sense of logic and order bear influence upon the present state of affairs. A coherent and continuous picture which makes good sense is sought.

For purpose of illustration, a vignette of a fairly typical case discussion will be outlined below.

The patient was an intelligent, refined, cultured man in his mid-thirties who had been married recently. Clinically his diagnosis was that of a compulsive-depressive with sporadic hysterical conversion symptoms and sporadic psychosomatic illnesses of a minor nature. Although his work record was excellent, he complained of feeling inadequate, obtained no pleasure from his activities, and "felt mildly depressed always." Despite this, he maintained an affectionate relationship to his wife, a warm and impulsive woman.

In the transference situation he developed a mild affectionate relationship which excluded expressions of hostility. His feelings toward the analyst and toward his wife were clearly associated with a childhood figure, his mother's younger sister, ten years his senior—a warm, rather seductive girl who lived in their house for many years.

His relationship to father had not been particularly close prior to adolescence, but this event ushered in a period of increasing ambivalence, rebellion, and estrangement. He described his father as a cold, imperious, calculating man, efficient in his business, and heartless in his human relations.

Mother was described as a beautiful but cold, depressive, and unintelligent woman who would continually nag and assume an attitude of reproach and pain. He stubbornly asserted that he had never loved her, but during the course of analysis we found that this stubborn assertion screened and denied his pre-oedipal attachment to her which had been disrupted by the birth of a sibling when he was three. Mother's younger sister, of course, served as the screen for his really very intense and heavily defended-against oedipal longing.

With the progression of treatment and in the context of transference developments, the patient recovered memories which eventually gave him a sense of conviction about the unconscious oedipal conflict which had been defended against by the highly negative view of his parents; with his father as a rival, and with his mother as defense against his sexual feelings. With the diminution of his own symptomatology he described his father as a strong and opinionated but nevertheless strikingly understanding person and his mother as a warm, giving, if somewhat narcissistic person.

As will be noted, a striking transition occurred during the course of therapy in this patient's historical impression of past persons and concurrently of past events. It need hardly be added that there was a specific consensus between patient and therapist that the latter view was a more realistic estimate of the character of his parents than was his former one, and that coincident with this, the patient improved markedly in the symptoms for which he sought help. Whether and to what degree that later description would be found to be more realistic by a jury of independent skilled observers remains a tantalizing question. That the above-described series of developments was part of an interaction helpful to the patient seems a reasonable conclusion. I may add my impression that the latter description of the parents hews more closely to the facts and that this modified inner experience was therapeutically useful, but where I would translate my impressions to certainty I am tempted to engage in elaborate and misleading phantasies and theorizing.

The Use and Misuse of History

Under the burden of the twentieth-century dictum that only claims of causality validated by the rules of scientific methodology can be true, there is a general tendency to translate historical data into specifically causal chains of events. Historical data, if conservatively used, may be of utilitarian value if they are not forced into the rigidly scientific model. The fact is that the scope of scientific methodology is not such as to be of much help in validating data of this sort even though, from other perspectives, it is true. When, however, under the guise of science, elaborate causal chains are postulated, little can be said for them except insofar is they may give the therapist a sense of security and become a means for arriving at a consensus with the patient. Certain historical data are no doubt relevant in broadening our understanding of a given personality, but to translate this into neat little systems is a feat of the imaginative sense.

The elaborate systems which have developed out of such thinking are illustrated by the following. There is an implicit assumption in some quarters, presumably scientifically validated from incontrovertible data, that human psychological development is completely orderly and proceeds according to some master plan. Further, that succeeding generations are little influenced by external events and that certain stable features such as a fixed pattern of psychosexual development exists and always existed as a constant and controlling characteristic of mankind. Whenever emotional disorders occur, obstructions in the normal course of this development are invoked as the *cause* of the disorder and never as a concomitant occurrence or as an effect itself of disordered function. Oriented toward disordered function, little is said about normal development although there is the implicit assumption that it is some idyllic state to be attained only by the few. It is further asserted that science, reason, and truth are the ultimate good and that they will set man free from his neurotic and fettered state. Through the exploration and understanding of the meaning of past events, the assumption is made that man will from then on be the author and master of his own history. He will be freed through the mastery of his own past history in which he has been a passive participant to create a present history of his own writing.

History in psychiatry and psychoanalysis is used to posit meaningful and causal relationships between prior events in the life of the patient and present modes of thinking and behaving. Even though therapeutic change may ensue through this approach, this does not *prove* that such prior events were in fact the sole or even the main cause of the observable change. Prior events, even when validatable, occur in a given context with numerous variables, and the choice of a specific one as being the cause of present disability requires more than simply establishing that it existed at that time. Despite the elaborate amount of theoretical speculation as to the historical origins of given emotional disorders there is no reason to believe that a given disorder would be replicable by no matter what skilled hands. Were this opportunity offered to the therapist he would himself find it untenable, falling back on the multiple variables and the impossibility of reproducing just the state of affairs, both internal and external, which might produce an equivalent disorder.

Since the experiences of an individual out of which his character and his neurosis are formed are unique to himself, no amount of broad generalizations from child development or other studies as to historical development can predict the particular organization of the personality of a specific individual. The inevitably fragmentary *remembered* history tells us of only certain facets of the development of this individual which are hopefully relevant to the therapeutic task. General laws and theories point general directions and cannot particularize for the individual. Such general laws tend to stem from equivalent experiences with similar patients and serve as inferential propositions for the therapist. These propositions help to determine his approach to the patient and no doubt sometimes color the patient's responsive approach to the therapist, even including the type of historical data supplied or not supplied by him. This in no sense denies the validity of a genetic historical approach as a mode of therapy; it does raise the question, however, of what use we are actually making of the stated, remembered, and even documented past events.

Insofar as the therapist tends to orient himself towards psychopathology, his interest in the remembered experience emphasizes those aspects of it which constitute resistance. Thus, he emphasizes its function as a screen for other more painful memories which have made for neurosis. However, such conscious memories are also constructive in that they constitute pathways of access to buried memories. In this respect they resemble the manifest dream and are thus intimately bound to and constitute the channel of access to the underlying content. The buried historical incident also is itself often falsely viewed as being a pathogenic agent when, in fact, the forces of repression in the form of anxiety, guilt, or other emotions have prevented it from taking its proper place in the personality. Actually, with the process of de-repression in therapy, the repressed memory assumes its appropriate role in personality function and may become a positive organizing force, no longer burdened by the repressive forces which had made for the disordered emotional state.

History as a Living Process

The role of memories of prior experiences in establishing and maintaining a sense of identity and fullness as a person has been much emphasized in the literary field as well as in the field of personality study. Denied a historical view of himself, man would lack all direction and purpose in his life. He would be driven to create a curriculum vitae for himself as surely as those who have been deprived of sensory impressions are driven to create false ones in the form of hallucinations. Were he not to do this, his existence would become one of utter chaos. The amnesic states in psychiatry are but illustrations of the degree of disorganization ensuing upon the loss of the historical sense. Of course, where gross memory defects occur as in some organic brain syndromes, the degree to which the memory of prior experiences is depended upon for basic orienta-

THE MEANING OF HISTORY

tion to the self and to the world becomes blatantly obvious. Who I am, what I do, and what plans for the future I have made are functions of memory and of history, whatever else they may be. Man has no being without a history and a memory of past events, but this is a matter in the present and should not be reified into a dead ghost of the past.

As may be seen, a relativistic view of history has been presented. While the most careful documentation of past events is urged, at the same time the inevitability of their interpretation as events in the present is pointed out. The virtues of careful documentation rest in the fact that by these means, the present modes of behavior of patients can be most clearly understood. This does not suggest that such past events can be known in themselves other than in the most limited sense. The present interest of the examiner of history will always determine his perspective on it, and this knowledge can make for a more intelligent use of historical data in therapy. There has been a too naïve acceptance of history in this field in the past, and certain directions for fruitful research suggest themselves. Thus, an attempt to validate formally the historical figures constructed by different independent psychiatrists of the same family group, insofar as the congruence or lack of it is concerned, would be of great value. Another potentially fruitful direction for study would be to compare descriptions of reported individuals with actual interviews of the same individuals and thus to underwrite—partially at least—the level of coincidence of such constructions. In addition, in such situations where more than one member of a family group is in treatment the opportunity for such comparisons would be considerable.

The view of history presented underwrites the living nature of history as a continuing part of the therapeutic process itself. Thus the opinions held in some quarters that one takes a formal history at the beginning of the therapeutic process and that this version becomes a fixed image excludes the heart of the historical process. History is in a constant state of change, and during the process of therapy, the original historical picture inevitably undergoes significant change. Without some such change in the patient's imagery it is doubtful whether one can say that therapy has been successfully conducted.

THE SECOND LOOK

We regularly seek for truth based on a current interpretation of prior events. This is the case even though we may later deny the truth of yesterday's view of history only to establish a new version today. This is no idle intellectual game, since our present beliefs are powerful motivators of behavior. Such interpretations and their behavioral concomitants are the subject matter of science— that which science examines—rather than being science itself. This is not to take a negative view of either the inner version of truth which motivates behavior or of the scientific method, but rather to place each in its proper place in the field of personality study. In the process of psychotherapy some hypotheses are necessary if an intelligent approach is to be made to the patient as a person and as an historical figure. To assume that faith and good will on the therapist's part, however virtuous these traits, are all that is necessary, is to assume that the historical approach can neither offer truth nor utility. Needless to say, this violates our experience.

IV

THE SIGNIFICANCE OF THE ACTUAL HISTORICAL EVENT

―――――――――― ···➤◉◗―··· ――――――――――

Memory and Validation

In the search for anamnestic data in any sphere of medicine including the psychological one, the tacit assumption is made that a historical or developmental approach will reveal factors of importance. In physiological disordered states, in addition to obtaining a history attempts are made to supplement and validate the historical information by means of various laboratory tests and by the physical examination of the patient. The essential emphasis is placed upon the validatable historical event. As opposed to this, in psychological medicine the reported historical event is of central importance whether or not it can be validated, since it constitutes a reported event of psychological significance to the patient. There are occasions even in the latter, however, where the need to validate reported historical events becomes a matter of primary importance both as a research endeavor and as a necessary condition for the conduct of therapy.

While there is no question but that past experiences are imprinted in some fashion and thus influence thinking, feeling, and behavior, it is quite another matter to validate the occurrence of any specific historical event and to appraise its specific impact on personality organization. Events have a sense of reality for the patient whether they coincide with actual external events or not. This is not to say that such coincidence is a matter of no moment. In the study of history itself the distinction is made between propaganda and history. In the former, events are distorted for particular ends while in the latter great care is used, insofar is it is possible, to verify and reproduce as close an image as documents and the intuition of the historian will permit.

The memory of past events both as idea and feeling should ideally constitute a means of avoiding the repetition of past errors and also of perseverating successful patterns of performance. Or, more informally, we say that "we learn from experience." In the emotional disorders, a critical role is played by the dysfunction of the memory process, limiting learning and making for the repetition of maladaptive behavior. Also, in the instance of young children, the limitation of this adaptive process is conspicuously visible. They live only in the present, since they have no historically organic ideas in mind. Thus, historical reconstruction is an intrinsic part of the process of therapy. An attempt is made to see the patient and have him see himself in some continuing context in which his present modes of experiencing and of dealing with himself and others are a logical outgrowth. This historical reconstruction asks us to meet what, on the face of it, would appear to be the simplest of conditions. It requires a verbal statement of why a total mass of evidence draws us to a given conclusion and no other one and why and how this conclusion would be different if significant elements of the evidence had been different. Unfortunately, to meet these conditions in any absolute sense is impossible, and we can do no more than strive toward this goal.

What is commonly described as an historical event is composed of the actual happening and assumptions about the meaning of the happening. These are usually so fused together that the tendency is not to realize that other than an actual happening is being reported. If the patient states that he had thus and such an experience with his father at age five, this is not simply reported or presently experienced as cold fact devoid of meaning. By implication or direct statement it is an interpretative communication with which the therapist may or may not concur, and if he does not, he must eventually be prepared to offer alternate interpretations. Perhaps a sample of a physical phenomenon will emphasize the degree to which we are dependent upon assumptions about events. We say the electricity is "on," hence the room is illuminated. There is the assumption that some kind of force not to be seen is being communicated through the wire to a tungsten filament and is illuminating the room. Just so, we engage in similar propositions about human behavior, be it our own or others. In the above instance, it is implied that the son's version of the happening with his father derived from anger or love or jealousy, etc.

Earlier Studies on Memory and Actuality

As further background to the question of what attitude should be taken toward the reported history, it is useful to trace the ways that others have struggled with this problem in the past, with a greater or lesser degree of success. An old and tantalizing problem with which Freud, among others, struggled—namely whether a cultural or endopsychic view of memory was more accurate—remains a puzzle and is often mentioned as a classic example of the role of the memory of past events. Originally, he maintained that actual infantile seduction—a specific environmental traumatic event—was the source of neurosis. He later modified this to say that the actual infantile experiences of his patients in regard to sexual matters were not necessarily different in essentials from the norm. (He now put primary emphasis on the role of repression in producing neurosis.) He concluded that the history of infantile seductions reported by his patient were, in fact, fantasies and protected the child from the memories of his own sexual roles and actions. Interestingly enough, while he offered no validatable data to sustain one or the other view, the change in his theoretical position is often quoted by his opponents to belittle him—as if the second version had been validated! Within the therapeutic context, his shift from the cultural to the endopsychic frame of reference was fortuitous. From then on attention was centered upon the patient's modes of dealing with the actual event, his experiences, and his techniques for incorporating it. The patient was henceforth envisioned as an active, dynamic unit capable of change rather than a passive receptacle of the buffets of fate.

The more specific question of the nature of childhood amnesias and of screen memories has an important bearing upon the matter of the validation of past events. Freud, in his consideration of screen memories, emphasized the repressive nature of amnesia, while for purposes of contrast Schachtel is a good representative of those who have stressed the cultural origins of such amnesias. The relevance in the present context has to do with the credence which can or cannot be placed on the actuality of the remembered event. The concept of screen memories has been a most useful dynamic formulation. For some reason, however, its original meaning has been modified in common usage through the years to convey that both the screen memory and that which it conceals are of a more than psychological significance, and constitute actual specific events. The term "screen memories" was introduced by Freud in 1899 to describe certain defensive operations by which memories of apparently little significance represented displacements and modes of concealing memories of far greater emotional significance. In his paper on that subject there are several interspersed comments, not particularly relevant to his main theme, which bear on the present topic. Thus, he states:

> There is in general no guarantee of the data produced by our memory . . . It is very possible that in the course of this process [the means by which a repressed phantasy makes contact with a memory trace] the childhood scene itself undergoes changes; I regard it as certain that falsification of memory may be brought about in this way too.

With some astuteness he indicates where memories have been falsified, but the second version—however more convincing in the psychological and therapeutic sense it may be—can lay only limited claim to coincidence with the actuality of past events. Thus he closes with:

> It may indeed be questioned whether we have any memories at all from our childhood; memories relating to our childhood may be all that we possess. Our childhood memories show us our earliest years not as they were but as they appeared at the later periods when the memories were aroused. In these periods of arousal, the childhood memories did not, as people are accustomed to say, emerge; they were formed at that time, and a number of motives, with no concern for historical accuracy, had a part in forming them, as well as in the selection of the memories themselves.

Schachtel discusses the normal amnesias of childhood and postulates that the culturally imposed categories of memory available to the adult are not suitable vehicles for the experiencing of childhood memories. He maintains that the modes of experiencing of childhood are only minimally available to the adult and that this accounts for the great bulk of normal adult amnesia of childhood events. While he mentions the amnesia of repression, this is marginal to his central thesis. Thus even when childhood events can be absolutely validated this is not in itself proof that they will be of psychological meaning and value to the adult, since the forces of repression are supplemented by the differing modes of experiencing in child and adult. He stressed the stereotyped modes of reporting prior events common to the adults in a given culture with its emphasis on the culturally acceptable. Events are not only reported in this manner, they are perceived and experienced in this manner, and on looking back at one's own prior experiences they are subject to this same process.

Freud's later writings include a further statement on the question of reconstructions in which he again emphasized the importance of the memory of events rather than the actuality of events in therapy. Thus he states:

> . . . the path that starts from the analyst's constructions [reconstructions] ought to end in the patient's recollection; but it does not always lead so far. Quite often we do not succeed in bringing the patient to recollect what has been repressed. Instead of that, if the analysis is carried out correctly, we produce in him an assured conviction of the truth of the construction which achieves the same therapeutic result as a recaptured memory. The problem of what the circumstances are in which this occurs and of how it is possible that what appears to be an incomplete substitute should nevertheless produce a complete result . . . all of this is material for a later inquiry.[1]

Since then, the question of the importance of the validation of reconstructions has been taken up by others. Thus Reider, in discussing a specific reconstruction associated with therapeutic progress, states:[2]

---

[1] Sigmund Freud, "Constructions in Analysis," in the *Collected Papers of Sigmund Freud* 5: 358–71 (London: Hogarth Press, 1937).

[2] N. Reider, "Reconstruction and Screen Function," *J. Amer. Psychoanal. Ass.* 1(3):389–405.

One last point should be remembered. It is now justifiable to ask whether the reconstruction has actual validity as an event, or whether it is a condensation of a set of circumstances within the conditions of the particular time in the patient's life. . . . most of the patient's symptoms could be shown to be derived out of either the truly actual past events (the reconstruction) or the childhood situation (as represented by the reconstruction). *Either one or the other is true, or both. To argue the point further would be only spurious and tendentious, since interpretations and reconstructions are at best but approximations.* [Italics by author.]

In effect, Reider dismisses the issue as an irrelevancy. Several years later, Rosen reintroduced the idea that the validation of a specific event may be of importance even in therapy. He describes a case where the reconstruction of the mother's attempted suicide during the patient's third year is substantiated when the patient confronts his father with it. Father's prior denial seemed to be an important factor in the patient's illness. He states: "In this paper the formulation offered, unlike Reider's, would tend to assert that, at least where the symptom of derealization is concerned, the question of the actuality of the reconstructed event is of more than academic importance."[3]

That the subject remains of great interest is illustrated by the more recent paper of Ekstein and Rangell. They offer cautions against rash reconstructions and recommend the empirical study of children (direct observation) and clinical experimentation to validate theoretical positions. They are more clear about what to be wary of than in what to accept in a given patient. In fact, at one point the comment is made that a given reconstruction was "confirmed by several memories" of the patient. Unfortunately, they do not attempt to further spell out the conditions for validation of any given historical event.

In the above brief review of some relevant contributions to the nature of the process of memory and thus of history, certain issues were emphasized. First, the question of the importance of the external event as opposed to the endopsychic experience of the event; second, the influence of the adult state both in its repressive as-

[3] V. H. Rosen, "The Reconstruction of a Traumatic Childhood Event in the Case of Derealization," *J. Amer. Psychoanal. Ass.* 3(2): 211–21, 1955.

pects and in respect to the unalterable characterological changes pursuant to maturation as influences on memory; and last, the question of whether the validation of reconstructions as specific events is or is not of major importance in psychiatry and psychoanalysis.

When Is Validation Important?

It should be made clear that what is under examination in this chapter is not the validity of the experiences as experiences or of the memories as memories. The specific matter under consideration here is when and under what circumstances such experiences and memories can, with some finality, be said to coincide with external reality—with actuality. For the present purposes, prior events will be assumed to have a specific pattern. It is self-evident that the same event will be perceived and experienced and hence reported in different fashions by the various participants. This is even more particularly true of the affect-laden events which the patient brings to the treatment situation. Nevertheless, a common-sense view dictates the assumption that such prior events have a kernel of specific facts which will be referred to as the actual event. Another arbitrary ordering of events commonly used in psychiatry will be employed. Recent and remote past will be referred to as somewhat different sorts of events. This has the virtue of a certain degree of naturalness, as witness the consistent order of diminution of memory in such organic brain conditions as are observed in the senile. It is common practice to consider the very recent past, today's events, as current and to omit thinking of them in historical context. However, anything which we think about including the moment just past is an historical event and will be so considered here.

While superficially it would appear that a view of history based exclusively on the memory of the patient would meet all of the needs in the psychiatric and psychoanalytic context, such proves not to be the case. There are instances where the determination of whether a past event actually did occur becomes a matter of critical importance. For instance, a college student reports that the other fellows in the dormitory are calling him a "fairy" and bounce a ball against the door of his room every evening. The matter of whether his peers are actually carrying out these acts is of major importance; are these reported events actually occurring and are they thus a measure of the young man's accuracy of perception, or are they projections and thus a measure of possibly profound mental illness?

It is not only in such instances as the above, where potentially paranoid mechanisms are in process, that the therapist has occasion to be concerned with the actuality of events. An example of quite a different area where the therapist may choose to attempt to ascertain the actuality of events is the following one. In a severe neurotic depressive state a patient reported that his income had dropped sharply during the past few months. The therapist attempted to explore this incident from the standpoint of the over-reactive nature of the depressive response, the veiled guilt, and so on; but met with no success. Finally he insisted, against some resistance on the patient's part, that he total his receipts for that period of time, and the patient reported that no decrease in income had occurred. Only then could the dynamics of his depression be explored.

The above examples raise a series of questions relevant to the therapeutic process quite aside from the matter of the patient's particular inner experience of the remembered event.

1. When does the actuality of events become a matter of prime importance to the therapist?

2. What does he accept as sufficient validation of such events?

3. What degree of conflict is there between the search for validation for its research possibilities and the therapeutic process?

4. Is there a difference in orientation between attempts, in the therapeutic situation, to validate the actuality of events in the recent past as opposed to the distant past? If so, where is the cut-off point?

5. In using the principle of the credibility of the reported events as some measure of their actuality are we not using a screening device to exclude many possibilities which could not have occurred?

6. Can the therapeutic situation itself be used as an instrument to measure the actuality of events other than itself?

7. What are the common pitfalls in attempting to validate historical events?

This chapter will limit itself to some comments on these questions since, in truth, no complete answers are available to them.

As cited above in the examples of the bouncing ball and the distortion of financial receipts, the degree of accuracy of the reporting of validatable events can be a matter of major importance. What general principle makes for this assumption? Why can we not simply say that the given version is plausible or not plausible, concur or not as the case may be, and let it go at that? In the previous chapter, certain specific instances were cited where it was felt that this principle applied. There are, however, certain states where the normal processes of judgment are felt to be sufficiently impaired as to necessitate the attempt, either via the patient or others, to validate specific events. For instance, in the child, in the psychotic, and in such states as somnambulism and other fugue states these conditions clearly prevail. In some circumstances the reconstruction of events from either the distant or recent past require validation. Thus, Rosen was able to reconstruct an event from his patient's infancy and to suggest that the patient attempt to validate it from his father. As regards the recent past, a reconstruction which proved to be valid was based upon the demonstrated neurotic tendency on the patient's part to cheat his wife, the income tax people, and so on. The particular reconstruction, which proved to be accurate, was that the patient had grossly understated his income on entering treatment in order to be seen at a reduced fee.

A particularly gross example in which validation for reported events may be sought either at the beginning of or even during the course of a psychoanalysis is that which arises when physical symptoms suggestive of an organic disease process are disclosed. In these circumstances the patient is referred for the appropriate examination, X-rays, and other studies in the attempt to validate the history given by him. Thus, during the course of a psychoanalysis an analysand reported—and this is history in the making—symptoms suggestive of a perforating duodenal ulcer. Recourse was had to an internist for validation of the suspected diagnosis, and further validation was obtained during the following necessary surgery. Curiously enough, when questions of the relevance of validation are being discussed, events of this kind which have both a physical and psychological impact are usually ignored.

While one motive for the many humorous anecdotes about psychiatry and psychoanalysis is most certainly resistance, the concealed truth in such humor deserves serious consideration. A recent actual incident came to my attention. A prominent judge telephoned a psychiatric hospital to inquire about a friend of his who was suffering from chronic alcoholism. He spoke to the patient's physician, who informed him that the patient suffered from the delusion that he was related to a certain member of the royalty. Of course, such proved to be the case, as was well known to the judge. It would be easy indeed to dismiss this humorous episode and the somewhat caustic manner of the judge as indicative of the typical obtuseness of the lawyer towards the psychiatric point of view. But the fact is that such incidents happen more often than we are even aware of, and the lawyer has wide experience too in attempting to establish matters of fact and in amassing convincing proof to establish such facts.

What would be considered to be sufficient proof in psychiatry and psychoanalysis that the ball had actually been bounced on the student's door and that his peers had called him a "fairy"? Many of us would be content with an appraisal of the student's character, the presence or absence of supporting evidence in the remainder of the history and, on some occasions, opinions from relatives or potential participants in the incident. The request for more definitive proof would likely be met with the judgment that further inquiry would be redundant, "obsessional," or even worse. The fact is that little short of seeing the ball bounced on the door or not seeing it when the ball is allegedly being bounced on the door would constitute such proof, and the same is true of the alleged verbal assault. It would require the actual proof of the psychiatrist's own senses or of other neutral observers. Opinions from the alleged participants might or might not be trustworthy, and certainly the opinions of other non-observers would be of no help in validation. This is a particularly gross sample of an event of the immediate past. If one considers the subtle innuendoes and interplays in events of even the recent past, the possibilities of validating events of the remote past are slim indeed. We are largely dependent on frequently honestly conflicting versions of events which have been differently experienced in the first place and then differently altered in the course of events. In therapy only a limited amount of help can be obtained from the occasional old diaries and other documents of this sort.

Studies in Validation

Even in otherwise carefully conducted scientific work, certain assumptions about the memory of past events are made that bear on the present topic. Penfield describes in connection with the electrical stimulation of the temporal lobe of a series of patients, the following:

> The experiences recalled are chiefly auditory or visual, or else they are combined auditory and visual. Curiously enough, there are no examples of recall of a time when the individual was devoting himself to his own action—no example of a time of eating, or of sexual experience, or of concentrated reasoning, or running a race, or singing, or playing the piano. There are many examples of hearing complicated music, sometimes accompanied by seeing the scene in which the music was originally heard and feeling the emotion that it produced.[4]

In another publication[5] he discusses a memory of an event which allegedly occurred seven years before. At the time of examination the patient was fourteen years of age. This event is presumed to be corroborated by the mother's memory of the reporting of the incident and by the patient's two brothers (age unstated) who witnessed the event and recalled it. It need hardly be said that any incident is liable to false consensus and particularly so an event of seven years before, when a girl seven years old is alleged to have been approached by a man stating "How would you like to get into this bag with the snakes?" This represents one of a great many reported cases, and for the most part no validation of any sort is offered for the alleged events.

That these patients reported extensive experience is unquestionable and that some of them were experienced as recall of prior event by the patient is clear. What relevance they may or may not

---

[4] W. Penfield, Twenty-sixth Hughlings Jackson Memorial Lecture, 1961, in *Med. News* 17(14).

[5] Penfield, W. and Rassmussen, T. *The Cerebral Cortex in Man* (New York: Macmillan, 1950), p. 164.

have had to prior actual experience is a subject unto itself and would be much more difficult to validate.

Several studies of a statistical nature in the more specifically psychiatric field have thrown a degree of light on the characteristics of memory and on the complexities to be dealt with in the matter of recall. They aim to prove certain general theses related to recall which might well be useful in the general theory of memory phenomena. Unfortunately these very principles limit but do not deny their usefulness with the individual patient. The conclusions must inevitably have a degree of generality which prevents their direct use to validate the memories of any given patient. If successful, they will provide more accurate generalities to substantiate or substitute for the ones we are presently employing, and this itself is no small accomplishment.

Haggard, Brekstad, and Skard interviewed mothers before the child was born and reinterviewed them at several fixed periods for the next 7–8 years. Some of their conclusions seem obvious to us, others less so. The mothers' anamneses did not reflect their earlier experiences and attitudes so much as their current picture of the past. Anxiety at the time of the interview served to distort the accurate recall of many experiences. However, anxiety at the time of the past experience seemed to facilitate recall. What the informant said depended in part on the relationship between her and the interviewer and on how the questions are phrased by the one and interpreted by the other. The length of the time interval by itself was not meaningfully related to the reliability of the anamnestic reports.

In another study by Goddard, Broder, and Wenar a series of mothers upon whom adequate clinical records were available were interviewed for 5–6 years later in connection with such elementary facts as the duration of gestation, etc. They found that some kinds of history such as the duration of nursing are apt to be grossly distorted, while other kinds of information such as the increments of weight at various periods are accurate. In this preliminary study no conclusions were offered but some suggestive findings were reported including the fact that almost one-half of the major illnesses that the child had had were not reported. An earlier study had arrived at very similar results.

SIGNIFICANCE OF THE ACTUAL EVENT

Conflicts Between Research and Clinical Practice

Despite opinions to the contrary, in the actual conduct of psychotherapy and psychoanalysis there are many situations where the process of research and of therapy are in conflict. In the attempt to assist the patient to explore the basis for his symptoms and therapeutically to modify them, great emphasis is placed upon the inner conflicts of motivation and of unresolved intrapsychic tensions. It is his mode of perceiving the world and his means of dealing with it that interests us, and we are interested in history only insofar as it throws light on his reactions. The aim is to understand history with the patient and to use this knowledge to modify neurotic automatisms. With the emphasis thus placed squarely upon the patient and his experiences, introducing other actual persons of significance into the scene as additional sources of information or even excessive preoccupation with the issue of validation in the two-person situation may well vitiate the basic therapeutic framework. As might be expected, the more serious the emotional disorder the less disruptive the introduction of other persons will be. This has to do with the fact that the patient's capacity to cope with his problems as a primary intrapsychic process is proportionately reduced and makes for a modification of both the aims and process of therapy.

There are two ways in which the term "research" is used in the field of psychological medicine which have made for much confusion. One has to do with the exploration with the patient of his intrapsychic processes and, insofar as it has to do with history, of his description of his experiences with others. The other has to do with the attempt systematically to validate the assumptions and hypotheses that may or may not have originated in the first-named process. It is this latter process that is often seriously in conflict with the therapeutic process and here, more than in many other areas of science, the probe may so alter the thing to be examined as to grossly limit the possibilities of validation.

As may be observed in the two studies already cited of the memory of mothers, the requirements of the scientific approach are such as to insist upon the reduction of the number of variables to a number which will allow for the possibility of significant results. Unfortunately, the therapeutic situation is such as to make such studies of ancillary importance but not of critical aid in dealing with the infinite variables which are present in a given patient. The therapist is, in this respect, rather more in the role of the historian than of the social scientist. Much of what he has to do with is of an irreducible level of complexity and is not replicable. As with the historian many intelligent assumptions may be made, but relatively little absolute proof is possible.

In the usual situation, the opportunities to validate events of the recent or immediate past are greater than for the more remote past. The fact of the possible availability of other witnesses in itself argues strongly for this. Unfortunately, however, it is just the very events of the distant past that are apt to throw the greatest light on the development of emotional illness. The tendency to lay emphasis on characterological development and hence upon the events of the remote past as opposed to the recent acute traumatic event is common to both general psychiatry and to psychoanalysis. The more recent de-emphasis on the reactive type of depression and the increased emphasis on depression as an intrapsychic state, primarily, which is unique to the individual and dependent on his particular modes of dealing with stress, are indicative of this trend.

The recall of past events, as has been emphasized by Haggard et al., is heavily colored by the anxiety at the time of the interview and by attitudes toward the interviewer, and this is the impression one obtains from clinical practice. Unfortunately, however, clinical practice does not lend itself to the proof of this. While it is common for the patient to claim better recall during periods of greater comfort, this is useful in therapy as a measure of his experience but cannot be used as validating evidence. The therapeutic situation itself is a highly colored, emotional one, and the patient is prone unconsciously to conceal and distort historical data for reasons of defense, and sometimes consciously to do so because of attitudes he may have toward the therapist. The opposite of this is often the case, and the patient may unconsciously supply false data in an attempt to gratify or placate the therapist or for other reasons and "tell the therapist what he wants to hear."

The studies previously quoted suggest that certain classes of data tend to be more clearly remembered than other classes of data. This is an intriguing finding, but the clinical situation with individual patients does not clearly indicate any patterning which definitely transcends the possibility of personal bias.

The Rationality of History

The next matter of interest is the question of whether the credibility of events is not in itself a useful screening device. There are many rational versions of history, but not all versions are rational. Were the young man who claimed that his school fellows had molested him to have also stated that they had horns in the middle of their foreheads, this would stretch the limits of credibility and would raise considerable question about the validity of the entire reported event. Unfortunately it is sometimes these additional distortions that tempt us to overlook the considerable segments of accurately reported history which accompanies the distortion. This same issue makes for recurrent critical clinical problems. Thus, the patient with a long history of hysterical conversion symptoms involving one or another area of the body is peculiarly vulnerable to the neglect of even serious organic states since he is felt to be an unreliable informant. It is sometimes a difficult clinical problem in fact to determine when one has to do with yet another conversion symptom and where the symptom constitutes actual physical organic disease. To determine when an adequate physical examination must be insisted upon and when it would represent a maneuver that would simply reinforce the tendency to conversion is often a tantalizing issue.

An anecdotal example is that of the patient who actually felt compelled to protect himself against the assumption that he was hallucinating. A depressed man who had ground privileges in a mental hospital near Baltimore, where alligators are not a common part of the population, observed a small alligator in a nearby wooded area. Knowing that if he returned to the hospital and reported what he had seen that only one conclusion would be drawn, he captured the animal and brought it back to the hospital. Evidently someone had brought it back from a more tropical climate and, when it grew too large, had released it in the woods. While the actuality of distortions of sensory experiences is not being questioned, constant alertness is necessary to ascertain the possibility of the actuality of reported events of even the most psychotic patients.

Since we have actual experiences with our patients, the question naturally arises as to the degree to which the credibility of the patient's reporting may be calibrated on the basis of experience with him, and this principle will be considered along with some common sources of error in the use of it. In clinical practice a consistently constructed life history offers valuable clues as to character development and probable modes of experiencing life and of behaving. Also, some useful clues may be obtained from disparities and omissions in the history as well as from what seems consistent in it. Thus, the omission of a period of time in the history for which no memories are available is clinically suggestive of some event or events of significance that are omitted for one reason or another. It must be emphasized that such a clinical suggestion is not a rule, but it is a clue to possible lines of inquiry which may be profitable. It is suggestive, but in itself proves nothing.

In the therapeutic situation the therapist has the opportunity to appraise the validity of prior events he himself has experienced with the patient. Through his own immediate experiences he has the opportunity to appraise the patient's ability to communicate at least more recent historical events and this is, to a degree, a measure of the patient's capacity to describe accurately experiences with persons other than the therapist. This is by no means an altogether trustworthy gauge since not infrequently the patient may be grossly more disorganized in the treatment situation than in other situations or vice versa, and this may make for an accordingly wide disparity in his reporting of events. Certainly every therapist has had patients who present essentially psychotic symptomatology in the consultation room and who, at the end of a session, will almost physically pull themselves together and go out to present a not unusual picture in their other human associations. Accepting the above limitations, however, particularly in prolonged treatment, the therapist is aware of a broad spectrum of personal experiences with the patient, and on the basis of this, he establishes some estimate of the reliability of the patient as an informant. In the therapeutic situation it is common to observe wide fluctuations in the patient's memory even about a specific historical event, this being dependent on the level of anxiety and the concomitant character of the defenses at any given time. But, as treatment progresses a more consistent and probably more accurate version of history is established.

Common Errors in Appraising Historical Data

As has been previously emphasized, no actual historical event can be viewed as being divorced from the meaning of the event as an incident of greater or lesser significance in the patient's life. Particularly in view of the great difficulty in securing validation for any such event, certain common errors in assigning meaning deserve mention. Perhaps one of the commonest sources of error is that of overlooking the plurality of causes for any historical event. While it is true that some causes have a greater degree of relevance than others, it is a matter of particular importance not simply to embrace a specific cause. This should be done in a particularly circumspect way if it is a cause which fits neatly into one's preconceived theoretical notions. This inevitably makes for the neglect of alternate possibilities and the neglect of subtle differences between apparently similar events. The matter of multi-determination of causes sometimes disposes to a particular dilemma in psychoanalysis where this is a formalized concept. This theory is of considerable value but readily lends itself to misuse since it can be used to defend a closed theoretical system. In that instance if, for instance, one of a series of fixed theoretical views is found to be inapplicable as an explanation, another of the same series is invoked. While lip service is given to multi-determination the view is invoked that one or another member of the series is the principal cause and that the complex structuring of causality is essentially rejected. This is well illustrated by the sharp difference between the classic and the cultural schools in psychoanalysis, where each group rejects summarily the claims of causality of the other and likely some truth rests with both.

Another common source of error is the failure to envision an historical event in a chain of continuity and to view it instead as a first cause. This may occur not only in connection with verbally reported events but also in connection with events actually observed. If one observes a patient strike another this is an actual event, but it may be of limited meaning unless, for instance, one knew that it was in response to a prior unseen assault. Even in the two-person therapeutic situation, no doubt some share of the patient's positive or negative behavior toward the therapist constitute events which are responsive to the therapist's behavior, which even in the best of circumstances is only partially consciously known to the therapist himself. Thus, some aspects of historical events can always be said to have antecedents which one can only know more or less about but never know in their entirety. It is frequently the case, and particularly where the opportunities to validate events are minimal, to resort to reasoning after the fact. Much of the reconstructions of the history of the factors making for emotional disorder must suffer to a greater or lesser degree from this fallacy, since there is no possibility of replicating the precise circumstances leading to this particular person's emotional illness. The best we can hope to do is to keep this factor minimal.

When it is the therapist's appraisal that the distortions of the patient are consistent with community attitudes and are thus no more than commonly held prejudices, it is his judgment that they do not in themselves suggest emotional disorder. Needless to say, in some circumstances, such attitudes may become the vehicle for the expression of personal emotional difficulties. An example of a potential distortion of past events based in prior history is that of the patient's account of particular attitudes he has experienced toward members of a minority group commonly looked down upon in a given community. In these circumstances, the therapist may find the given attitude of little importance in connection with the present illness of the patient. That is to say that the therapist's role is something other than that of the champion of non-prejudicial opinion. If the distortion of past events is considered to be unique to the individual, not altogether plausible, or as suggested above, common to the social group but overweighted by the patient, then the stated past events out of which they are alleged to have arisen become subjects for exploration in treatment.

V

IF YOU SAY GOOD MORNING, YOU'RE A HYPOCRITE

--- ...—◉◀—... ---

The Primary Importance of Verbal Communication

Historical data as well as other information are obtained and recorded in verbal form. Therefore, the communicative process,
especially verbal communication, has been the center of a considerable amount of interest and study in psychiatry and psychoanalysis.
In the present considerations no attempt will be made to survey the
extensive literature in the field. However, certain special deficits in
the exchange of information will be considered which are illustrative of the kinds of interference in communication which are found
in the therapeutic approach to the emotional disorders. Particular
attention is directed to these defects since they bear heavily on how
the messages from the patient are to be understood, and hence on
how history itself is to be understood.

Some patients lack an understanding of various levels of information exchange and will respond idiosyncratically as a result.
They seem to be unable to discriminate between these different
levels, and thus are unable to deal with the complexities of interactions with others. As a result they are prone to respond with
anxiety, hostility, and withdrawal. A typical example of this phenomenon has been chosen as the title for this chapter. Thus, the figura-
tive and literal sense of "good morning" as a mode of greeting of the
most superficial sort, as a wish that the recipient have a good
morning, or as a quality of the particular morning itself, seem not

59

to be readily discriminated. In more profound instances of such disturbances, the deficit in discrimination extends to such distinctions as between "morning" and "mourning" and so on.

Verbal communication is organized so as to permit the transmission of a broad variety of meanings. As a consequence, there is a series of possible intentions in connection with the use of any given word or phrase. Within a fairly broad range, there is a reasonable amount of agreement about which of the multiple possibilities are relevant in any given instance. Of course, there are frequent errors and misinterpretations, but while the study of psychopathology is prone to emphasize these, the actual degree of successful communication is indeed remarkable. Of course, in addition to the words themselves there is ancillary help from inflections, gestures, touching, etc.—but the words themselves are the central device.

Due emphasis, however, should be placed upon the many occasions when a consensus about the meaning of a particular word or phrase is assumed to exist, while in fact some subtantial misunderstanding has occurred. One of the common phrases employed by today's adolescent generation to describe its sexual activity is to "make out." Insofar as this is not elaborated upon, it may include the entire span of physical sexual activity from holding hands to having sexual intercourse. It is possible to err in both directions in connection with the interpretation of a term of this sort and to infer less—or more—extensive sexual contact than has actually occurred. This is particularly prone to happen when the historian himself has assigned some specific if spurious meaning to the word.

The particular context in which a word or phrase is used throws important light on its meaning. For example, consider the ordinary social transaction which occurs when two casual acquaintances meet and one asks the other "How are you?" and the response is "I'm fine." This is commonly understood as having little to do with the specific meaning of the words themselves. In truth, if they are taken in their literal sense, serious question may be raised about the integrative capacities of the person who so interprets them. He lacks the ability to discriminate levels of relationship, which speaks of potentially serious personality defects. In other instances, the external meaning of the word is the relevant one and, in the same terms, a non-acceptance of its literal meaning would infer excessive suspiciousness and potential rejection of fruitful relationships. Thus, there are those who cannot use the phrase "I love you" since they are aware of some measure of ambivalence in their relationship to another. If, however, such an expression of feeling would wait for the total disappearance of ambivalence in human beings, it would never be used.

Words may serve multiple purposes in addition to their communicative function. They may become reified into things, may become weighted with emotion and become primarily carriers of it, and they may become means of dampening down the emotions and of controlling and sometimes suppressing them. While these various characteristics of words are presented as absolute categories for purposes of classification, in actual fact there is a considerable degree of overlap between them in any actual verbal communication. The important matter is one of the balance between the various functions of language.

Non-Verbal Cues Which Give Meaning to Language

In normal circumstances there is a wide variety of cueing devices which assist in determining the context within which a given statement is to be understood. The incapacity to appreciate the appropriate context for a given word or phrase is apt to be seen in states of severe disorganization, namely in the borderline states and in the schizophrenic disorders. Bleuler has emphasized that the only meaning of the essence of a thing is a teleological one. It is essential, therefore, to be able to discriminate common points of interest and of consensus in order to be able to understand the meaning of words. He states the matter in the following terms:

> The idea of water is quite different depending on whether it refers to chemistry, physiology, navigation, landscape, inundation, or source of power. Each of these special ideas becomes connected with the other ideas by a quite different set of threads. No healthy person thinks of soda water when his house is being swept away by a flood; nor will he think of water as a medium of transportation when he is thirsty.[1]

[1] Eugen Bleuler, *Dementia Praecox: Dementia Praecox or the group of schizophrenias* (New York: International Universities Press, 1950), p. 16.

In addition to the immediate contextual relationship of a given word, there is a broader system of cues based on the appraisal of the persons from whom the message is being received and on the wider social meaning of a given message. There is a series of internal processes which a given message must undergo if it is to be understood. This is, of course, contingent on the adequacy of the physical sensory perceptions. There is a range of incoming messages varying from the ones which are heavily laden with affect to ones which are primarily cognitive. In the former, various possibilities of the meaning of a given communication within the social context are sorted and an inner decision is made as to its meaning. This depends upon the individual's prior experiences and upon his capacity to come to some appreciation of the communicator's feeling state and intent. This, in turn, is based upon a variety of non-verbal cues and his own "feel" for the situation. When words are used primarily as communicators of affect, a considerable degree of sensitivity and empathy on the historian's part is required. In these circumstances he must not become preoccupied with the precise meaning of terms, and in the process miss out on the feeling the informant is trying to communicate. Many of the common curse words are of this nature, where it is conceivable but not likely that specific questions of bastardy, incest, etc., are being referred to. In a majority of such instances they represent modes of communicating feeling, but the specific nature of the feeling cannot be directly inferred from the term itself. Meaning on such occasions is to be found in inflection of voice, the context in which it is used, and an appraisal of the general mood of the patient.

By contrast, at the opposite extreme from these heavily affective kinds of communication there is a class of communications which tends to concern itself with abstract relationships, as for instance the language of mathematics. Here the intent is to reduce the communication to the specific meaning of the stated message itself. In both, however, initial processing and appraising must be carried out to differing degrees before appropriate responses can be made. If the message is understood it may be directly responded to, or it may be responded to with questions intended to clarify it, or it may even be ignored.

IF YOU SAY GOOD MORNING, YOU'RE A HYPOCRITE

The Cultural Context of Language

The social context within which a given communication is to be understood is a situation of a very high level of complexity. The parents, as cultural carriers, introduce their children to this process of discrimination by means of a long and arduous period of training. In many quarters the social frame of reference is simply communicated as a matter of moral precept. No matter which framework is used, such principles are an attempt to institutionalize a complex series of functions. Thus, from very early, the child is exposed to situations where the parents share certain information and experiences—including, and especially, their sexual life—from which he is excluded. In the same terms, he himself, as a member of the family group, is taught that there are certain confidential situations which may be verbalized and discussed within the family group but are not to be discussed with others. Children are prone to react with a simple acceptance of these precepts, with passive compliance, or with rebellion. This will depend upon the given clue as well as upon the nature of their relationship with their parents.

The problem of discriminating spheres of allowable communication is sometimes a prominent feature in the emotional disorders and may be a serious problem for the patient to cope with in communicating relevant data to others. Some parents will extend the necessary rules having to do with communications to include prohibitions on what may be experienced intrapsychically. Thus, the child is told that thinking about certain things or having feelings about them is forbidden and "bad." Such views have been formalized in certain religious groups where it is maintained that since the thought is parent to the act, the thought is itself sinful. In this connection, in the normal process of discovery of his own boundaries the child discovers that "mother cannot know what he is thinking." This may, for example, derive from experimenting with lying. A consequence of this is the discovery of a private world within which certain thoughts and feelings can be concealed from the parents with impunity. Given that prior experience has not eventuated in a too harsh superego, this world of private experience serves as a mode of partial discharge for feelings in phantasy by means of veiled communication. If, however, the superego is too severe, even this potential channel of discharge is denied.

Certain ethnic subgroups, as well as the adolescent subculture, are illustrative of the tendency to deal with those whom they perceive to be their elders as if they were the children. They accordingly create a rather loose but elaborate vocabulary which is fully understandable only within their subculture. Typical of this kind of word is "ratfink" which cannot be clearly defined but seems to be a strongly valuative and affective descriptive term. Often commonly used words are used in special contexts. Thus, the term "signify" is used by the American Negro in a variety of contexts, none of which are relevant to the dictionary definition of the word. When persons of other than the given subculture begin to use a given word from this special language, the meaning of the word is reversed, another word is chosen, or some other means is sought to assure privacy of language and to establish the m-group as a separate entity.

The need to discriminate the level of relationship occurs both in the individual and at group level. The "rules of the game" apply all the way from "good morning" to international affairs. It has been said by some that the lack of capacity to discriminate the difference in quality of relationships between the internal affairs of a nation and its foreign policy, with the consequent tendency to apply the rules of relationship appropriate to internal affairs to international affairs, has in fact interfered with the work of the United States in its conduct of foreign policy.

What is under consideration here is not the question of morality as such. Truthfulness has adaptive capacity, and there is good reason for the community to take a dim view of truly hypocritical and untrustworthy behavior. This is something other and different from the various modes and techniques by which relationships between individuals and in groups are controlled. Just as truthfulness is often a necessary adaptive function so are these deviations from a rigid, puritanical version of absolute truth. The "rules" are not incontrovertible, and the decision to follow them, revolt against them, or to change them benefits from the recognition of their existence. In addition, it is necessary to know the rules in order to interpret the cues and other behavior of those who do use them. For example, to choose the social structure as a point of reference, the decision on the part of the parents to abide by certain edicts of their religion, to violate others, and to conceal the violations discreetly, is often seen by children as hypocrisy. Depending on one's point of view and one's knowledge of cultural attitudes, however, this may or may not be judged to be the case.

The rules of confidentiality and of what orders of things may or may not be communicated, to which persons, and in which contexts, are necessary adaptive devices in order for the individual to function within a group and in order for the group itself to be operative. For individuals or groups to function, it seems essential that certain sorts of communication be maintained and that certain kinds of data be excluded. These latter are of a kind which represent a threat to the individual or group if communicated, since they interfere with the capacity to relate in a constructive way. In connection with this, the child is taught the values of truth, but in certain situations, the value of evasion and of the "white lie."

The group generally requires a high level of compliance, including language usage, as a condition for membership. In this connection the psychopathological state of *folie à deux* is relevant. In it, the dependent member of the pair carries out an adaptive function within this given two-person culture when he takes on the manners and language characteristic of the dominant one. When this relationship is disrupted, he tends to revert to the usual social habits in these regards. Some of the same characteristics may be observed in the broader social culture where, in certain special circumstances, given modes of behavior, lanaguage, and attitudes at variance with usual behavior are adopted. The proverbial attitudes of the soldier, including his socially approved attitudes toward killing, are samples of this. His attitudes are reflected in his special usage of language also, as might be anticipated.

Language and Psychopathology

All communications have, as one of their characteristics, the capacity to invite greater intimacy or to function as distancing devices. The casual communication, such as "Good morning," or "How are you?" or the responsive, "I'm feeling fine," are approaches to another person of a rather casual and peripheral nature, but viewed in another context, they are intended to be non-communicative and distancing devices. They even suggest, in some contexts, that further inquiry would be intrusive and that the level of intimacy must be maintained at a very superficial level. In other contexts, they may represent tentative approaches to very great intimacy. While the signal may be a faint one in either direction for normal persons, the borderline patient or the schizophrenic is often acutely sensitive to such signals. The integrity of these patients is very fragile and even the most peripheral degree of closeness may be experienced as a massive and terrifying invasion which must be avoided. In these circumstances the most casual comment, insofar as it is itself an approach to them or insofar as it invites potentially greater closeness on their part, may be experienced as a dire threat. Consistent with the perceived threat, the motives of the other person may be impugned, and he is accused of having concealed designs under the ostensibly benign and casual comment.

The therapist may find himself in a veritable contest with such patients. The patient is torn between the desire for intimacy and even the merging with another, and his dread of total loss of his identity if his wish is realized. This will reflect itself in his responses. Thus, he may even invite frankness from the therapist and then take the expressed content itself as an offense. In the opposite direction, if the patient senses any withdrawal on the therapist's part he may experience an immense sense of threat in turn. This, of course, makes for a constant therapeutic dilemma since it is difficult to maintain the optimal degree of relationship in order to permit the therapeutic task to continue. The patient himself may employ modes of behavior the motivation for which he obscures from himself, and it is not always clear even to the therapist when a given statement or course of action is expressive of positive feelings and when it is a mode of discharging hostile ones, since either may be involved in inner conflict. Thus, in the ostensible attempt to be frank and truthful, the patient can be brutally truthful and very hurtful. This allows him the expression of hurtful impulses under a veil of virtue.

One of the most important reasons why the patient identifies another as the hypocrite is to cope with his own conflictual and contradictory drives and defenses. The device of projection reduces inner turmoil by assigning one side of a conflict to the therapist. For instance, the patient whose superego is dictating a course which demands giving up of a desired instinctual gratification may cope with the conflict by projecting his superego and accusing the therapist of nefarious designs. In the same vein, the insistence on the absolute truth from the therapist may be the expression of the use of falsehood by the patient which is then projected onto the therapist.

Related to the projective defenses, but somewhat different in kind, is the general class of relevant transference phenomena. Where the patient has, in the past, experienced hypocritical behavior or ordinary social behavior that was interpreted by him as hypocritical, he responds to the therapist in the same fashion that he responded to past emotionally charged figures. In these circumstances, the actual verbal content in the present situation is substantially irrelevant since even the most indifferent message may be interpreted by him according to his special needs.

As opposed to the projective and transference situation, the patient actually may be responding to hypocritical messages which are going on in the present. This is something that may be overlooked in the mentally disturbed. In view of the distortions of reality which they have in some spheres, there is often a tendency to discredit all observations and judgments they may make. This is not infrequently done at the expense of valid judgments the patient may be making. Especially when the therapist himself is the object of censure is there the tendency to assume that it is a projective defense on the patient's part. This may be used by the therapist as a mode of warding off valid criticisms, and if it is so used, it will interfere with the therapeutic process.

In general, the likelihood of countertransference reactions is greater in the group of borderline and schizophrenic patients. This derives from the increased likelihood of projective identifications with these patients on the therapist's part. These differ from ordinary projections in that the object upon whom the impulse is projected is not experienced as ego-alien. The object is empathized with, but there is an accompanying unconscious need to control the patient, since he now represents the feared and projected impulse. In these circumstances the patient's criticisms of the therapist are especially apt to be interpreted as "symptoms" since, by so doing, the therapist can ward off his fear of his own projected impulses.

There is a group of somewhat more chaotic disruptions of the communicative process in which the sense of personal identity is centrally involved. They manifest themselves as markedly contradictory appraisals of the actuality of one's performance, including verbal performance, and the inner affective experience of the same events. Thus, what the patient himself may intellectually judge to be a good performance is experienced affectively by him as the opposite. This is based on his derogatory self-evaluation. Insofar as his reality sense is reasonably intact, the contradiction between actuality and his inner conviction is the source of great anxiety and confusion. This both intensifies and is intensified by a disrupted and wildly fluctuating sense of self. Concomitantly, his inner appraisal of verbal behavior is similarly affected, and this grossly affects communication. The use of words takes on special importance and, if successful, may serve to structure both him and his environment. If this process breaks down, however, it may constitute an important segment of the presenting picture and a problem in communication of major proportions.

Illustrative of this phenomenon is a young woman twenty-three years old who diagnostically falls in the never-never land between the borderline states and the schizophrenic disorders. She became ill at eighteen when she entered college and was separated from her family for the first time. Her presenting symptoms, which have continued essentially unaltered, were an accentuation of difficulty in sleeping described as "lying awake trying to keep thoughts out of my mind," "feelings of tension," "inability to remember things," and a "general feeling of confusion." She stated that she was "entering into her second self," that there was "the sense of having a barrier between myself and others," "there is a lack of communication," with the feeling that her "thoughts and words did not penetrate the barrier and that those outside could not penetrate and communicate with me in turn." She felt intrigued by this "strange, eerie second self" but at the same time was panicky and fearful of "losing contact with the outer world and never being able to re-establish it." This very patient did indeed challenge the sincerity of a "good morning" addressed to her.

These seriously disturbed patients are especially apt to raise the tantalizing question as to whether a primary psycho-physiologic communicative deficit may be the first cause of the affective difficulties, the disturbances in identity, and the whole of the inner chaos. Whether or not a physicalistic or psychological first cause exists, they both seem to be factors which, once established, will potentiate each other. Just so, an integration of psychodynamic and psychophysiologic modes of thinking will make for a broader approach to the theoretical and practical aspects of therapy itself.

Parallels Between Information Processing and Repression

The ability to recognize and employ cueing devices in order to transmit and receive messages has been amply demonstrated. There is substantial evidence that deficits in these areas derive from earlier life experiences. As has been the case in the past, however, a more sophisticated present version of information processing allows for extensions of psychological theory. For instance, the study of schizophrenic language has been, before now, largely directed toward the manifest language and its interpretation. This derived from the fact that it was felt to be the only available channel of approach to the thought processes which were assumed to be a deficit. However, this approach offered no opportunity to localize the deficit. Was it global in character, at the input end of the system, at the motor (output) end, or somewhere in between? With these limitations, emphasis was placed on the tendency toward concreteness in word usage with consequent idiosyncratic and noncommunicative language. By clinical means alone there seemed to be no way to demonstrate whether this was a defect in processing of incoming stimuli or a deficit on the motor side of the system.

More recent studies of sensory deprivation and suggestive pioneering studies of sensory overloading seem to indicate, in a psychophysiologic sense, that there are physical processes which parallel and are perhaps correlated with the psychological process of repression. The emphasis upon the role of repression in psychopathology, as a source of symptomatology, has tended to obscure its constructive function. Repression has as its manifest function the exclusion of certain psychic content from consciousness, and in this sense is maladaptive in that it denies to the patient some segment of experience and thus of reality. In addition, however, it may deny access to consciousness to some data as a part of the adaptive process and may be a necessary condition for the smooth functioning of the organism. This includes the preconscious registration of incoming stimuli never consciously experienced, and the motor discharge in equivalent terms. Such stimuli originate both from within the individual himself—for instance, his drives—and from the external environment. The registration of incoming stimuli which have not been conscious has been extensively demonstrated, and the motor discharge in the same terms is a matter of common observation. Thus, it has been said that the centipede would be nonfunctional if he had to think before he moved each leg. In terms of language itself, the actual saying of "good morning" as a kind of greeting is more often than not preconsciously derived and is of this same nature.

In the preoccupation with disordered psychic functioning the emphasis has been, of necessity, upon the process of bringing unconscious ideation and feeling into consciousness. The intent in such instances is to increase the scope of reality and to permit a controlled reorganization of malfunctioning states. This goal de-emphasizes the constructive role of automatic preconscious and unconscious modes of thinking, feeling, and behaving. From this point of view, much of what is called "insight" is a studied attempt to bring about constructive change in disordered states and might be said to be a departure from normal modes of functioning. It implies a level of self-consciousness that is intrusive on smooth functioning.

While no exception is being taken to the disruptive force of some varieties of repression, its capacity to maintain the stimuli to be dealt with at an optimal level gives it a constructive function as well. If, either for reasons of the massive amount of incoming stimuli or because of limitations in the capacity to cope with them, such stimuli would be disruptive, repression of them becomes a constructive event. While it is useful to be able to cope with ambiguity without resort to the exclusion of some aspects of a situation, this is true only within the limits of the capacity of the individual. Beyond this, screening-out becomes a necessary function if confusion and disorganization are to be avoided. The superego is, under normal conditions, an excellent example of a functional system which operates largely out of awareness. It is the transmitter of the culture, and it commonly does so by a series of automatic, unconscious messages. However, since the malfunctioning superego is often a significant factor in the emotional disorders, there has been some tendency to neglect its large unconscious and automatic mode of functioning in the normal state. In normal circumstances, the superego is hardly noticeable as a separate system and certainly has little access to consciousness.

Viewed from the psychophysiologic point of view, the ability to process stimuli depends on the rate of intake of such stimuli. It has been demonstrated that a basic amount of external stimuli is necessary in order to maintain integration. In the state of sensory deprivation, the subject has extensive phantasies and even hallucinations. Of particular interest in connection with the subject under consideration here is a related area which lends itself less well to formal research, namely the effect of overloading the normal subject with stimuli or the effect of a normal load of stimuli upon a subject who is unable to cope with them. Its relevance to the matter of language derives from the fact that, in ordinary circumstances, many incoming verbal stimuli are screened out as a necessary part of the communicative process. The screening process likely occurs, not as simple inattention, but through the process of denying such stimuli access to consciousness although they are registered preconsciously. In effect, they undergo a process of repression. There is ample reason to look upon the process of the registering of certain stimuli and the discharge of motor responses as an active rather than a passive one. It might be said that the lack of awareness of certain stimuli is a factor of simple selective inattention rather than of active repression. This is not a passive process, however, and such stimuli are directed into unconscious channels. The evidence for this is their impact upon psychic life and the fact that they can elicit motor discharge even without specific awareness.

If, thus, the screening of stimuli and the process of healthy repression are necessary conditions for adequate functioning, then the breakdown of this screening device becomes a matter of special interest. Clinical observations of the effect of the inability

71

to process and repress incoming stimuli as a result of a defect or change in sensory end organs are available. In the process of learning itself, numerous sounds are screened out. In fact, this is one of the problems in becoming accustomed to a hearing aid, where the learned process of hearing is circumvented. In an intriguing study of the emotional repercussions to stapes mobilization operations, the problem in readjusting to a normal load of sensory stimuli after long continued adjustment to reduced stimuli was marked. Better hearing was responded to negatively, and these patients resented the successful operation.

There has been some relevant research which tends to bear out these findings. It is in the particular sphere of research in schizophrenics but may well have broader applicability to normal and neurotic persons as well. There seems to be some measure of consensus in various studies that the deficit in schizophrenic language resides in the areas of initial organization of incoming data and the areas in which incoming stimuli are processed. This is to say that the deficit is neither in the sensory organs nor in the motor areas as such. Most importantly, the disordered speech in schizophrenia does not seem to be representative of disordered "thought process," as has been the common concept in psychiatry.

The experimental evidence suggests that the deficit is in the sphere of the capacity to screen incoming stimuli, either in the phase of initial organization or cortically. In the first instance, it is felt that schizophrenics are unable to screen out irrelevant incoming sensory data, and this results in an overloading of short-term memory systems. This may derive from the slow rate at which information is processed in schizophrenics, with loss of data due to the limitation on time in which the short-term system can hold data. This resultant loss of data might account for the thought disorders and bizarreness of language and behavior. Data are simply presented too fast to be efficiently handled. In this version, catatonia constitutes a social withdrawal as a protection against excessive stimulation. An intriguing study by Usdansky and Chapman tends to corroborate the schizophrenic-like consequences of a deficit in data processing which result from overloading in normal subjects. Whether one views the deficit as one of data processing, perhaps based on biochemical deficits, or as a breakdown of normal psychological defense mechanisms with the subsequent overwhelming impact of incoming stimuli, both theories argue for the imperative function of adequate screening and the cancelling out of alternate possibilities if the schizophrenic state is to be avoided. While the frame of reference of psychodynamics and that of the psychophysiologic studies just considered would appear quite disparate, such is not the case. The crucial factor in the communicative deficit in psychodynamics resides in the modes of coping with anxiety in patients, who, for reasons of earlier experiences and their particular responses to them, are unable to deal with interpersonal stresses in the usual way. In addition, clinical observations as well as research studies have demonstrated that anxiety reduces the capacity to process incoming data. As opposed to this, psychophysiologic deficit may itself be the source of anxiety. It may thus be seen that both of these factors potentiate each other and that there is no essential contradiction between the psychic and the physiologic sources of communication deficits.

While the primary interest in this chapter has been in the verbal modes of communication and their vicissitudes, a part of that which has been presented has relevance to much broader spheres of interpersonal transactions. Thus, in some circumstances, even objectively available data may be screened out as an adaptive function for some persons. Further, the intrusion of certain kinds of factual data about a teacher into the student-teacher relationship may well influence the use of the teacher in his specific role by the student and therefore interfere with the learning process. Screening out such data on the student's part may well be adaptive in nature.

As may be seen, viewing the functions of repression and of the handling of communicative data in the fashion suggested, the negative aspects of repression are by no means ignored. They are, however, placed within a broader perspective in which the circumstances, the particular vulnerabilities of the person who is engaging in repression and his preconscious mental process become more evident. In persons with major deficits in the ability to identify various categories of incoming data, it would follow that gross misunderstanding, suspiciousness, and withdrawal would eventuate. Where data are identified too fast, the affective components mentioned undoubtedly would in turn reduce discriminating capacities.

Within this broader frame of reference the deficits in the understanding and exchange of information of the patient are at least somewhat less puzzling. The recognition of subtle cueing devices and the capacity to identify the meaning not only of simple words but of words which have a multiple series of meanings demand a high level of integration indeed. If interviewing and the collection of significant biographical data are to be carried out, they must be done with constant alertness for the capacity of the patient to receive and transmit data and with due cognizance for both the potential psychological and psychophysiological deficits in this area.

VI

WHY SOME PATIENTS CONDUCT ACTUAL INVESTIGATIONS OF THEIR BIOGRAPHIES

····━━●◉●━━····

The Limitations of Verbal Communication

Just as there is good reason to emphasize the significance of verbal communication, there are some circumstances in which behavior rather than words is the necessary condition for historical investigation and therapeutic progress. It is not an uncommon observation that—in connection with the introspective process of dynamic psychotherapy and psychoanalysis as well as in the general process of self-exploration for that matter—there is an urge on the part of some to explore old diaries and papers and to return to the physical settings and persons important in an earlier period in life. This need may be felt only during the treatment process itself, or it may have been felt before then. If successful, it enhances the available biographical data in both a factual and emotional sense.

Often, in the psychotherapeutic or psychoanalytic situation, there would appear to be some resistance to conducting such an exploration into actual past situations that parallels the resistance to talking about certain subjects. This resistance frequently manifests itself as a tendency simply to forget to carry out an intended exploration, or as is often the case with such conflictual situations, to engage in such explorations in a substantially unconscious fashion only to discover in midstream, as it were, that they are in process. This phenomenon will be illustrated in the course of this chapter.

Every therapist and analyst has sometimes felt called upon to analyze such resistances with the result that actual scenes from childhood, etc., are revisited. In addition, such behavior sometimes is accompanied by the stirring up of old memories and feelings which are useful in the furtherance of the psychotherapeutic or psychoanalytic investigation.

Psychotherapy and psychoanalysis, despite their interest in and capacity to cope with the emotions, are heavily dependent on verbal process for their investigative and therapeutic applications. The capacity, or potential capacity, to think before acting and to think and to experience in lieu of acting on occasion is one of the necessary conditions for the conduct of psychotherapy and psychoanalysis. These abilities are intimately involved with verbal process, both as a part of internal experience (or communication within the individual person) and as a part of communication with another person. As a corollary to this, the faculty of introspection, the process of self-examination, is essential to the psychotherapeutic and the psychoanalytic process.

One of the resultants among others of this necessary emphasis on verbal process has been a tendency to view behavioral patterns as being intrusive upon the main business of exploring the defenses and resistances through which aberrant thought and behavior arise. As a general principle this seems valid enough; however, this is sometimes distorted to mean that all behavior is inadmissible and indicative of neurosis—which is of course an absurdity. This is illustrated by the gradual extension of the term "acting-out," which was originally intended to describe the "living-out" in the life situation of things which should be talked out in the analytic situation. Eventually this technique of defense, as first conceived, was extended to include all sorts of behavior which was felt to be neurotic in nature in the general sense. This has been further extended by some to describe any behavior of which they did not approve—as a kind of epithet. Depending upon the critic's own tendency to be more or less given to behavioral expression himself, the judgments would be more or less severe. In view of the propensity of the psychotherapists and the psychoanalysists as a group to be of an introspective turn of mind, their judgment of "acting-out" on the part of their patients tends sometimes to come rather too readily to mind.

WHY PATIENTS INVESTIGATE THEIR BIOGRAPHIES

Examples of Constructive Revisitations During Treatment

The first and most evident function of revisiting old scenes is in the interest of mastering the past. This thesis was developed by Freud using an analogy from the play of children. In it he advanced the view that children repeat unpleasurable experiences so that they can actively master a situation which they had first experienced passively. In the same connection, however, he posited the existence of drives that "push forward towards progress and the development of new forms." It is this latter aspect of the drive to re-explore old situations which will be considered here and which appears to have been somewhat submerged in current psychoanalytic theory.

Although examples of this process are common enough in essentially every case, several typical examples will be presented as illustrations of the phenomenon under consideration.

An obsessional young man in his early thirties came into analysis because of increasing anxiety associated with the disruption of his obsessional modalities. Five months after treatment began he planned a brief week-end trip to a nearby town. While driving there he felt impelled to continue the trip to his birthplace some 150 miles way. This latter town had not been visited by him since the age of six. On arriving there he parked in front of a quite modest house and began searching for the old family home which he had assumed to be a much more elaborate one. He eventually established that the very house in front of which he had parked—ostensibly by accident—was indeed the home of his first six years.

He continued his investigations and discovered a small playground where he and his brothers had played in the period before leaving the town. In it was a sliding board, now perceived as being of modest size, but heretofore remembered from childhood as being of terrifying height. A tiny stream recalled pleasant play as a child. Finally a block-square southern mansion near his home recalled an immense sense of lonesomeness accompanied by the ringing of church bells which was a dominant early screen memory.

This actual perceptual series of experiences proved to be crucial ones in the analytic process. The patient needed to go back and experience the past incident in more than its simple recall and verbal form. It had to have the affective impact in both the *pleasurable* and *painful* sense of being in the actual physical place.

A second example illustrative of the same theme is the following. A man in his mid-thirties with a rather typical obsessional character disorder had discovered only at age twenty that both of his parents had died during his childhood (his mother, when he was three months, and his father, when he was seven years of age), and that he had been the adoptive child of a maternal aunt since he was three months old. During the course of a first analysis the patient felt it necessary to go to the Bureau of Vital Statistics and actually to see the death certificates of his parents. Some five years later, during a period of re-analysis, he extended the above process and felt impelled to go to the gravesites of his parents and to visit the house where the family had lived when he was born. In his words of some years later, "There was present a feeling of the need and importance of establishing a very specific real knowledge of these matters. The general tendency and forces of earlier living— personal and external forces—had been to obscure these facts. This validation of facts and places I consider not 'acting-out' in the sense of acting in the service of not remembering but rather acting which reversed previous avoidance. Carrying it out required overcoming resistance and anxiety about it!"

Yet a third example of a similar process is that of a young woman who entered analysis because of the inability to become pregnant. This inability had intensified a long-standing dread that something was wrong with her. This, she felt, derived from a conviction which she had had since childhood that her parents shared some terrible secret about her. In developing her history, she recalled repeated painful and terrifying gynecological treatments between the ages of three and six, but she made no conscious connection between these treatments and "the secret." The patient had been told by her mother that these treatments were the result of the patient's having climbed on a fence and having fallen on a pointed wooden paling. Presumably, the consequence of this misbehavior was that she had "turned her womb upside down." The patient recalls being censured for being a "tomboy," and told that she might never have children. One further relevant memory of a later date was that on one occasion when the patient had had a slight vaginal discharge of no great consequence she had informed her mother. The mother

78

became quite agitated and angry and blurted out the name of a male relative at whom her anger seemed to be directed.

At the age of twenty-four, the patient confided these data to her fiancé, and he questioned the plausibility of the story. The patient then confronted her mother and discovered that at the age of three she had contracted childhood gonorrhea from the above-mentioned male relative who was then staying in the home. Although her mother had been assured that there was no reason to feel the patient would be sterile, this fear had persisted in both the patient and her mother.

During her analysis, the patient felt a strong need actually to see the house where the incidents described had occurred. She found herself revisiting the old neighborhood to see the house and the fence she was said to have climbed. The fence—in adult context—seemed benign. Along with all the anxiety of the visit there were elements of reassurance in it as well as a developing new outlook on these old, emotionally loaded experiences.

As an example of the bursting through of unresolved mourning precipitated by a physical setting from the past, there is the case of a man who entered a period of re-analysis some years after an initial period of analysis with an analyst who had died while this man was still his patient. On leaving after an hour, the patient quite automatically drove to the site where the house of his childhood had been. This house had been torn down, and as he looked at the empty lot, he burst into tears. Needless to say, this was related not only to the loss of his prior analyst, the loss of his father, etc., but to the discharge of feeling associated with a specific physical site heavily cathected from quite early in life.

It should be noted that all of these examples are marked by a certain compulsive need to carry out the given investigation, and by a mixture of pleasure and pain. Both the need to recapture and digest in present context some past experience and some manner of pleasure in the mastering were regularly present. There was a sense of gratification that comes with having established, through the physical setting, a certain firmness and reality in connection with situations which had had a dreamlike, and even sometimes a nightmarish, quality. In one instance a massive discharge of feeling was accompanied by a subsequent sense of relief. Finally, for each of these patients there was the sense, at least, of the analyst's approval of the behavioral pattern, although this could not be validated. It may be added that in discussions with other analysts, the sense that such investigations are a valid part of the analytic process seems quite general.

Revisitations as a Way of Overcoming the Isolation of Affect

While the bedrock of psychoanalysis is the analytic experience itself, including those aspects of it depending on the verbalized interpretation and subsequent insight, it is also true that the psychoanalytic process cannot be conducted *in vacuo*—abstracted from the present living experience of the analysand. In the dynamic psychotherapies the same can be said with perhaps less emphasis on interpretation but more emphasis on the present life experience of the patient. What essential ingredients to the psychotherapeutic and psychoanalytic process may be said to derive from the ensuing living experiences? Even when it is said that analysis must be conducted in a state of deprivation this is so only in relative terms, and in fact, the influx of a mass of pleasurable and unpleasurable external stimuli remains basic. While the above-mentioned incidents have a certain dramatic quality and were chosen to illustrate the especial relevance of correlating memories with actual past settings, they represent no more than an extension of a generally observed principle. One of the major advantages of the frequency of appointments in psychoanalysis is to allow time for the exploration of inner psychic process and to avoid preoccupation with the present life situation of the patient, both as a consequence of the actual reality situation and as a consequence of resistance. This is not to say that the present life situation of the patient is irrelevant, since it is the current setting for neurotic repetitive modes of behavior on the patient's part. It is from this that the aphorism arose, "When the patient becomes too preoccupied with the past it is the analyst's duty to bring up the present—and the reverse."

Some further comments about the use of words as opposed to other behavior are relevant to the issue under discussion. Words and language serve the purpose of conceptualizing situations preparatory to action. The result of such conceptualizations is the stimulation or the inhibition of action, as the case may be. A further use of words is that they may become the regressive substitutes for deeds. According to Freud, in the obsessional patient, almost invariably there is an early development and repression of the impulse to look, and this facilitates the regression from acting to thinking, from concrete to abstract modes of functioning. Of particular importance to the present thesis is the idea that the "advanced" process of thinking may, on occasion, actually represent a regressive phenomenon, contrary to the generally held view of its genetic direction. The resultant of this is that the transference situation, with its emphasis on ideation and verbalization sometimes potentiates and tends to stabilize neurotic tendencies.

Greenacre has had some relevant comments to make with regard to verbalization. She emphasizes the fact that speech itself, through the fluctuation of pitch and intensity, may represent acting-out rather than simple ideational process. In addition, she attempts to place these basically affective and other than simply verbal aspects of speech in a genetic context by reminding us that during the second year, speech, walking, and sphincter control are in the process of being mastered and that speech and walking may be influenced by the struggle for mastery of the excretory functions. Both bodily activity and the need to communicate, first in gesture and then in primitive words, are often related to efforts to control the excretory functions. Thus this intimate intermingling of word and act further emphasizes that either one can take on some characteristics of the other in later life.

Particularly in the obsessive-compulsive neuroses, although in other disorders to a degree as well, can we observe the resort to the omnipotence of words and the isolation of feeling. As Anna Freud states: "The obsessional patient does not fall silent; he speaks, even when in a state of resistance. But he severs the links between his associations and isolates ideas from affects when he is speaking, so that his associations seem as meaningless on a small scale as his obsessional symptoms on a large scale."[1] In optimal circumstances, the analysis of the patient's defenses against affect in the context of the transference situation may suffice to overcome the isolated

[1] Anna Freud, The Ego and the Mechanisms of Defense (New York: International Universities Press, 1946), p. 38.

affect. However, in some patients—and the cases already cited are examples of this—some further process seems necessary. In accord with this, doing as well as thinking constitutes a potential means of overcoming their isolation and precipitating a more emotional state. The obsessional neurotic abstracts himself from any situation; he is in the role of the intellectual observer rather than being a participant. If thinking is the preparation for action in the normal, in the obsessional the fear of action and its associated affect prompts him to use thinking regressively, as a defense. It is because of this that doing instead of thinking becomes a way of overcoming the isolation. Doing in this context is not simple impulsivity but also behavior in the interest of interrupting a regressive pattern and of lifting repression.

As is often evident in therapy, such patients tend to isolate emotion and ideation, and the treatment is in danger of being limited to an intellectual process only without an affective working through and with a poor therapeutic result. Just as there are recoveries of memories with the lifting of repression, so it is sometimes necessary to re-experience through the senses in order to lift such repressions. This may be expedited by actually visiting certain settings from the past or by actually seeing certain documents in order to experience the emotional impact of the returned memory and affect in a new perceptual context. In fact either the sensory experience itself may precipitate affect—and only then may the memory appear—or the sensory experience may mobilize a memory and only subsequent to this will affect be experienced. This parallels the equivalent process in memory phenomena where it is quite as equivocal whether the recovered memory is a product of the lifting of repression or whether the recovered memory itself acts in lifting repression or whether, in fact, these are concomitant processes.

Parallel with Déjà Vu *Experience*

In the experiences being examined in this chapter, the behavior pattern of actually physically returning to some setting is carried out in order to recapture memories and wishes and phantasies of the past as a mode of mastering anxiety. They reinvoke feelings of familiarity and invoke anxiety of a vague, uncanny sort. The impact of part of an old stimulus pattern reinvokes the total pattern as it was experienced in the past. They are in this sense emotionally of a kind with the *déjà vu* phenomenon, and like it, are attempts at reconstruction and of mastery. The sense of "I have been here before" seems to be connected with old conscious memories or unconscious experiences which are remobilized by exposing oneself to certain kinds of sensory stimulation.

The experiences under consideration bear a close resemblance to the *déjà vu* phenomenon, particularly insofar as the *déjà vu* may rest upon memories of prior experience. In the *déjà vu* phenomenon a present experience is felt to be repetitive of some prior one, and as is true of the phenomenon being considered, it is accompanied by a vague sense of unease and of the uncanny. It is said to derive from an anxiety-producing memory, wish, or phantasy, and the effort to ward off this anxiety. Prominent among the modes of dealing with this anxiety is the notion that the present anxiety situation has been successfully mastered in the past. In view of the difficulties in establishing any authoritative validation of many events, the memory–wish–phantasy complex is invoked to account for the historical basis upon which the presently experienced *déjà vu* is superimposed. That is, without prior experiences the present experience might not have been anxiety inducing, and in the reverse, without the anxiety of the present experience the memory, wish, or phantasy might not have been invoked as an antidote for the anxiety. In the actual revisitation, the ensuing anxiety meets with the reassuring experience of dealing with the realities of previously experienced objects.

The mastery of the traumatic event as a useful hypothesis is not only complicated by the previously mentioned difficulty in establishing the actuality of any given memory. In addition, we are faced with the dilemma of trying to establish when we have to do with a purely intrapsychic experience and when we might reasonably expect that a given behavioral pattern will ensue. For instance, it is a common impression in our culture that the criminal frequently experiences a compulsion to "return to the scene of the crime" in actual fact. There is, however, an absence of actual literature of other than a theoretical nature, and a prominent criminologist of many years experience is of the opinion that the actual act of returning to the scene of the crime on the part of the criminal is of the greatest rarity. This fact is of particular interest in that the theoretical notion of the attempt to relive and perhaps to master both the intense traumatic and pleasurable aspects of the crime, in the actual return appeals to a sense of the psychologically correct. In actual fact, it is a most uncommon behavioral event. It is probable that the understanding of the barriers and modes of translation of psychological into behavioral patterns and the reverse is quite limited in character, and because of this, the capacity to predict modes of behavior and the impact of certain actions on psychological experiences is limited.

Reorganizing Function of Revisitations

As has been mentioned, the urge towards mastery of a previously traumatic situation certainly plays a role in these revisitations. In addition, and perhaps more importantly, they function as a means of establishing certain aspects of reality in which the traumatic situation can be not only immunized but used as a focal point for reorganizations of a constructive sort. There is an intimate bond between the process of working-through and the particular class of experiences described in these patients. As I have described elsewhere, much of what is considered to be "working through" is preconscious, nonverbal, and highly affective in character. Such processes are tied not only to verbal modalities but to sensory impressions which flow in through all channels and function in the interest of just such reorganizing experiences.

Eventually when the experience is digested—and this may take one or more trips—the urge to go back dissipates. It would be the easiest course simply to assume that the previously traumatic situation has been mastered and that it was hence unnecessary to re-experience it. This position, however, leaves out of account the role of the repressed incident in the present personality integration. It is something more than that of an ingested foreign body to be extruded and gotten rid of. If reintegrated, it may well become a positive force in the reorganization of the personality incident to treatment. The first three examples given included crucial falsifications of the sense of self, and conspicuously in some, of crucial other persons as well. Although these distortions can hardly be looked upon as delusions in the commonly used sense of

84

the term, they are often very deeply held and are far from being readily amenable to critical discrimination.

On occasion, the seeking out of relatives and other significant persons from the past constitutes an important turning point in the process of self-discovery. This is often done in the expressed interest of checking on biographical data, but there is also the matter of reappraising these persons and often the corroboration or discrediting of certain attitudes toward their parents in relation to these other persons. Behind all of this is the reappraisal of oneself and the process of modifying the self-image and the sense of personal identity of the patient himself. The transference relationship and the identifications on the patient's part of the distortions intrinsic to it are often the bridge by means of which these further explorations can be made. As is the case of going back to old geographical settings, there is often significant resistance on the patient's part, and the act may finally come only after a long period of analysis and the gradual working-through of the resistance.

In this connection a recent report by Serota is of considerable interest. During the course of psychoanalysis he reviewed with three patients sequential films taken by their parents beginning with the earliest week of infancy. It was his impression that the photographic evidence along with the patient's accompanying verbal associations helped to elucidate evolving behavioral patterns involving the communicative modalities including affect, early efforts at motility, and social interactions. He found these films useful for the corroboration of data obtained from reconstructions in psychoanalysis. He did not elaborate on the circumstances in which the patient chose to introduce the films in this brief report other than to comment that several of his patients had privately reviewed the movies of themselves "apparently to stimulate memories." One would gather, by implication at least, that Serota found these experiences useful as corroboratory data, and that the actual experience for both the patient and himself helped further the analytic process in many less clearly intellectual fashions.

Contrast With Technique in Acting-Out Patient

There are usually three different approaches to the management of acting-out, with some degree of overlap between them. They are:

interpretation, prohibition, and strengthening of the ego. Interpretation represents the sharing with the patient of the underlying meaning of a given piece of behavior in the interest of establishing better ways of coping with his drives and defenses. The result is a greater awareness on the patient's part of the causes of maladaptive behavior. As a consequence, his behavior is apt to be more rational and less compulsive in nature. Thus, interpretation has as one of its goals—and this becomes highly relevant in the acting-out patient—the reduction of behavior in addition to changing its character. In the patients under consideration in this chapter, however, the goal of interpretation is the opposite. The result of interpretation is the actual physical as well as psychological re-exploration of the past, i.e., an invitation to behavior.

Prohibition, or the countermanding of certain behavior, is necessary in dealing with some impulsive patients. In fact, the terms of the therapeutic contract invoke certain conditions, including behavioral ones, if psychotherapy or psychoanalysis is to be conducted at all. While in many patients these derive from a mutual agreement between the patient and the treating person, those patients who are particularly given to acting-out will perceive the conditions for treatment itself as prohibitions. In some other situations, the treating person may actually use specific prohibitions in addition. In the patients described earlier in this chapter, on the contrary, the treating person often encourages them, however subtly, to conduct a planned exploration into their past. Regarding the last technique, strengthening of the ego, as a mode of dealing with impulsive behavior, it is one of the ultimate goals of treatment in the acting-out patient. This is the goal of the above mentioned technique of interpretations and of the stopgap of using prohibitions with these patients. In the acting-out patient one would hardly consider strengthening the ego by inviting more behavior. In the present group, however, strengthening of the ego derives from carrying out an exploratory act which then supplies data for further investigation in treatment but now in a new emotional context.

The exploration of old documents, the revisitation of physical settings, and the seeking out of significant persons from earlier in life are fairly common spontaneous modes of behavior both before and during psychotherapy and psychoanalysis. While these acts may constitute "acting-out" in some instances, in many more they constitute behavior in the interest of furthering the collection of affectively charged data and thus helping the treatment process. Treatment may be immeasurably benefited by the above mentioned investigations, particularly in those patients who tend to regress from acting to thinking. In such patients, the treatment situation itself may potentiate intellectual process and the isolation of affect. Exploratory behavior of the kinds mentioned, if affectively charged with a mixture of anxiety and the uncanny, and if supported with reassurance, can be therapeutic. Such behavior helps to overcome the isolation of affect and to integrate old experiences into the treatment situation. The result of this altered state of affairs is to open new opportunities for further explorations of the causes of present dysfunction.

VII

THE TECHNICAL USE OF HISTORY IN TREATMENT

Typical Problems

There are a variety of issues having to do with the use of history in the treatment process which deserve special attention. This is particularly true when historical data are laden with affect. Typical of the kind of technical problem which one sees is the use of historical reminiscences by the patient as a mode of defense. This obviates the examination of current events by him and intrudes upon his full affective participation in treatment.

Patients, and particularly obsessional ones, will use the cues offered by the treating person as a mode of defense against giving up their neurotic patterns. This is particularly true of historical events in those treatment plans in which the patient is invited to explore the genesis—that is, the historical development—of his symptoms and character development. To illustrate, a successful lawyer in his mid-thirties sought treatment with the complaint of increasing irritability, reduced sexual potency, and the recrudescence of a tic on the left side of his face which he had had earlier in his life for about a year between the ages of twelve and thirteen. In treatment itself he was, superficially, a model of co-operativeness. He was reasonable to a fault. If there were difficulties with his wife, employers, or colleagues, there was always some reasonable explanation for their behavior or he had been himself at fault. He supplied all sorts of "interesting" associations, phantasies, and dreams with every appearance of good will, but nothing seemed to change. In view of the rigidity of his character structure and modes of defense, especially vigorous attempts were made to explore the genesis of his difficulties. Here again, the patient was the image of co-operativeness, and indeed produced a deluge of historical data all of which seemed to be relevant. As treatment proceeded it became increasingly evident that he found the exploration of historical data a safe refuge. By means of it he could avoid facing the stresses of his present life situation. It proved that he was married to a woman who drank excessively and treated him quite brutally and that his excessive dependency on her made it impossible for him to cope with her in a realistic way. The genesis of his neurotic marriage and his neurotic mode of dealing with it no doubt rested in his past experiences and in his history. His general tendency to repress his anger, to develop reaction formations, and to turn his aggression against himself was particularly evident. The need to explore his past with him in the interest of changing these fixed patterns cannot be gainsaid, but the therapeutic dilemma was one of how to cope with a man who translated the very exploration of history itself into an additional obsessional device. In such circumstances the preferred technique is one of shifting the emphasis to the present without losing sight of the potential use of historical data when the patient becomes able to use it other than in the service of resisting change.

Closely related to the above, and often present in the same patient, is the use of intellectualization as a defense and the accompanying absence of the "working through" of the data so that he can attain useful insight. Many patients employ the defense of intellectualization using a variety of subjects for the purpose, but the intellectualization of historical reminiscences is a particularly common one. "Working through" has to do with the process through which things which are intellectually known by the patient become integrated in his character in such a fashion as to have a useful impact on his disorder. It is analogous to the difference between having "intellectual" knowledge about a given sphere of learning and having a "gut feeling" for the subject. Since the memories of the patient and the available history are of interest, especially insofar as they are potential means of bringing about constructive changes in him, the feelings associated with such historical data are crucial. With this in mind, some fundamental considerations relevant to the affects will be presented and correlated with the historical process.

The Crucial Role of Affect

The understanding in genetic, i.e., historical, terms of the origins of the neurotic process is considered by most schools of psychotherapy to be of crucial importance. Since there is usually a time lag between the acceptance of interpretations based upon such understanding and any therapeutic effect, the concept of "working through" was invoked. This concept rests heavily on the functions of the affects in their intrapersonal operations and in the two-person situation of treatment itself. It should be emphasized from the beginning that the major avenue of access to the affective life of the patient is by means of his subjective verbal reporting along with such analogies as may be drawn from equivalent affective experiences which the treating person himself may have had.

Of critical importance in treatment is the ability to engage in an emotional experience with another person. This must occur both in relationship to those affects which are a product of transference and those which are a product of the treatment situation itself as a unique life experience. In the transference situation it is necessary for the patient to be able to awaken and re-experience the old emotional states if therapy is to be successful. In it history is repeated in attentuated form and re-examined by means of a current replica of a historically significant person. The transference figure is not only *told* about old experiences, the old emotionally laden experiences are lived out in connection with him in a diluted form and in a form in which they can be detoxified. It should be noted that feelings have a history as surely as do physical events.

The capacity of human beings to interrupt repetitive patterns of feeling, thinking, and behaving, based in their prior experiences and thus in their history, is not possible without access to ideational process and to verbal techniques. It is nevertheless true that treatment must center much attention upon disturbing affective states. Of course this is in addition to concentrating upon the unconscious affective-ideational constellations, based in the patient's past history, from which his present difficulties derive. Not only is it necessary to concentrate upon given acute affective states but attention must be paid to the prevailing mood state against which background the given affect presents itself. For instance, a state of acute anxiety may be the superficial layer covering a predominantly depressive underlying mood. Such moods are complex states which may or may not be pathological in themselves. In dealing with a given affective facet of them, however, it is of the first importance to maintain a reasonable degree of stability in the over-all mood. This is the basis of the use of reassurance as a necessary accompaniment of any treatment. Often the verbalization, by the therapist, of the existence of a given affective state in the patient will serve as a channel for the emergence of this affective state. When a given affective state which is in repression gains access to consciousness and thus to a feeling experience, its potential pathogenicity is sharply reduced. In addition, the act of translating this feeling into verbal terms and of then sharing it with another person further reduces its pathogenicity.

There are complex interrelationships and subtle overlappings between ideational process and affects. Storch took issue with the tendency to speak of "emotionally toned ideas" as if they were rigid bodies in the unconscious. Since such definite thought formations do not exist in unchanging form anywhere, their existence is even less likely in the unconscious. In his words, " . . . in proportion as the periphery of consciousness is approached, the content of the idea loses more and more of its definiteness, becoming more undifferentiated and acquiring greater resemblance to emotion. The complexes which determine the pathological experiences, therefore, are not really unconscious emotionally toned thought formations, but rather vague, obscure tendencies and feelings of wholly indefinite ideational content."[1] What he has to say about pathological experiences can be legitimately extended to the character of unconscious mental operations in the absence of pathological functioning as well. In this latter state, it is simply less apparent.

Affect and Communication

Rycroft emphasized the communicative function of affects. In his view the most important fact about an affect is ". . . the fact

[1] Alfred Storch, The Primitive Archaic Forms of Inner Experience and Thought in Schizophrenia (New York: Nerv. and Ment. Dis. Pub. Co., 1924).

that it is perceptible by others and has an intrinsic tendency to evoke either an identical or complementary response in the perceiving object." The function of affects as a communicative device in interpersonal experiences has not been sufficiently stressed, and much is to be gained by viewing them in his terms. Insofar as we may consider the human personality as receiving important contributions through the internalization of historically significant persons, one might say that affects serve the same kind of function also in the internal economy. Intrapsychic activity is commonly seen as being something quite different from interpersonal activity, and insufficient stress has been given to intrapsychic communicative devices. Affects, thus, can be looked upon not only as having an important role in interpersonal communication but as having other critically important intrapsychic functions as well, a part of which is in the intrapersonal communicative process. An example is the function of the affect of anxiety as an internal signaling device when danger is perceived from one's own drives as well as from the external environment.

Behavior and expression include innumerable verbal and non-verbal means of communication, many of which precede the more advanced techniques of communication through language. These originate in a period of prehistory and are engraved by means of conditioned responses. They predate the remembered and verbalizable history given by the patient. In the adult, the intimate bonds between affect and behavior and expression as a means of interpersonal and intrapersonal communication persist and are a significant aspect of their function. While the communicative aspects of emotions are justifiably stressed, their role in stimulating behavior deserves more attention. Emotions have been described as "feeling with a cognitive attitude." The role of affect in stimulating communicative behavior, both verbal and non-verbal, is an important one. Thus the gestures and physical attitudes of patients are often analysable as communicative devices of affective states and, as a rule, are out of the awareness of the patients themselves.

The necessity to use knowing, i.e., conceptual, ideas to define feeling experiences makes for special difficulties. The process of scientific communication depends heavily on verbalization, and it can do only an impoverished job of describing and defining affect. As a result, the less definitive empathic and non-verbal communicative devices of appearance and gestures, voice tone, etc., are invoked to appreciate the patient's emotional state. To describe the emotions of fear, hate, guilt, or love—emotional states which are of such prime significance—in verbal terms, has tantalized the artist as well as the scientist. The artist has most closely approximated it when he has been able to arouse a resonant feeling in his audience; the scientist has been much less successful in his description of emotion insofar as he is bound to a more objective "non-emotional" verbal description.

The affects are the source of the color and richness of human experience. It is impossible to conceive of human existence without the manifold implications of emotions, and the history of the patient abounds with feeling. Even when the term, "lack of affect," is used in psychopathological states, it has reference to a relative reduction of the feeling state but by no means an absolute absence of it. No human relatedness is conceivable without affective participation. The very definition of affect includes both physiological and psychological aspects and they lend themselves only partially to examination. Insofar as strictly objective means are concerned, the physiological aspects of emotion are more available for study. Insofar as the psychological ones are concerned, reliance is placed upon introspective process or the verbally reported experiences of others.

Interaction of Affect and Ideation

The traditional separation of mental processes into affect, cognition, and conation has made for some convenience in our attempt to examine them individually. It has, however, interfered with the attempt to examine the total functioning personality, and various attempts have been made to consider the coalescence and interaction of these functional units. All attempts to fragment the flow of mental activity, no matter what the motivation may be, inevitably introduce artifacts into the stream of mental activity. The traditional separation of feeling as a mental function from thinking or knowing as another mental function has, along with its evident advantages, stultified the view of mental process as a unity. In this same connection, it is necessary that the structural theory in psychoanalysis be appropriately conceptualized in order to avoid a comparable kind of fragmentation. The id, ego, and superego are best compared, insofar as physical analogies are applicable, to three overlapping magnetic fields in a constant state of activity. There is ample justification for drawing lines of distinction between their variable functionable activities, but only if the amplitude of their interplay is not ignored.

Certain physiological processes tend to be associated with certain given affective states more often than with others. While no one-to-one correlation can be drawn between any given feeling and its physiological concomitants, some rule of thumb associations are employed to advantage. Thus, the probability that grinding of the teeth is associated with a rage state is immensely greater than is its association with love. Diarrhoea is apt to be a concomitant of acute anxiety rather than a state of pleasure. These types of associations have given rise to the proposition that "affect-equivalent states" exist and that they represent historically determined alternate channels for the "discharge of emotion" in the event that "discharge" through feeling and associated conscious motor action is denied.

Affect states and ideational process mutually influence each other, and it is unlikely that precedence can be assigned to one or the other of them in the adult. This also applies to memories and feelings connected with past events as well as current events. Suffice it to say that, when concepts and ideas are fragmented and faulty associations and conclusions result, there is often an accompanying affective disturbance, and vice versa. It is customary to view the ideational or affective disturbance as being primary and as the *cause* of the associated disturbance, presumably basing this upon the observable phenomena. To use a gross example, in the schizophrenias it is usually assumed that the ideational disturbances are the *cause* of the affective ones, while in the cyclothymic disorders the reverse is assumed to be the case. The more the dynamics of these illnesses are explored, however, the more reason is there to feel that they are concurrent interacting complexes of affect, ideation, and behavior where no such definitive concept of causality is warranted. To infer a linear concept is only to confuse the issue. These factors are interrelated and interacting; they mutually influence and stimulate or inhibit each other in a complex fashion which cannot be translated into simple cause-and-effect terms.

In addition to considering the impact of affect on ideation, it is necessary to consider that of affect on affect. It is not uncommon for one affect to replace another, at least in consciousness, and part of the task of treatment is to unravel the relationships between these historically determined affective states. This phenomenon is well illustrated by the complex function of wit, where repressed hostile, sexual, or otherwise historically unacceptable affective states are communicated by the substitution of more acceptable affective-ideational complexes.

Comparatively little formal attention has been paid to the constructive aspects of affective states. Even in connection with acute anxiety states, it is of considerable therapeutic importance to envision them as being not only disruptive psychopathological experiences but also as attempts at re-establishing a more stable and more constructive integration of the personality. One important function of even the acute affective state is to bring about constructive personality changes. In this regard, theory is perhaps more limited than is practice, since an operable level of emotional discomfort in patients has long been known to be a condition for treatment.

Out of the foregoing consideration of affects, something further may be said about a tantalizing problem. It is not uncommon for the patient to express great difficulty or an actual inability to describe his affective state in verbal terms, even though he may claim to experience it as a conscious, feeling state. Quite appropriately, the resistance aspects of this are first explored and, in fact, it often proves to be understandable in these terms. It is not infrequently the case, however, that one is left with a sense that the instances of this sort which cannot be understood are by no means all instances of resistance. Attention is centered on the overcoming of resistance as a therapeutic matter, since such conflictual areas are potentially alterable.

The instances of inability to verbalize an affective state, where there is reason to assume that they are not a product of resistance, are based upon the peculiar nature and origins of the affects. Having their roots in our visceral and skeletal selves from the earliest time of life, they are by no means always evident as feelings. Insofar as they are not, the capacity to translate them into conceptual and verbal form is proportionately limited. The greater the degree of regression, the greater is the difficulty in employing verbal forms to describe emotional states. This is in inverse proportion to the empathic appraisal of the intensity of the patient's affectivity and also of his degree of conscious feeling. The very concept of empathy gives cognizance to the above-described limitation of conceptualization and verbalization as communicative processes. In this same connection, there has been an increasing interest in the channels of nonverbal communication. It is only relatively recently, however, that they have been the subject of intense scrutiny. Such channels afford access to unconscious processes which the patient excludes from consciousness through resistance or which he is unable to communicate by any other means through the very nature of his experience. As Ferenczi has stated, the infant establishes communication with the external world by such feeling speech as crying and crowing before it learns to walk.

The Process of "Working Through"

The delay in the development of a satisfactory affect theory has been in large part responsible for the failure to understand the process of working through. Insofar as affect is considered only as a signal device or as a convenient mode of discharge it played a relatively minor role in theoretical formulations. Affect is a prime and historically determined mover in psychic activity, and affective patterns of experiencing and of response are more resistant to change than are cognitive ones. In fact, man's relative lability of response and his capacity to master his environment are closely correlated with his intelligence and ability to use verbal symbols, with the resultant capacity to alter his automatizations of feeling and behaving based in his past experiences and his memory of them. The automatic affective response is therefore more characteristic of children and of lower animals, and stereotypies are proportionately more common in the latter, i.e., those of the nature of conditioned phenomena. As would be anticipated, they are also more common in the regressed states found in the neuroses and psychoses.

It is a truism that the full affective experiencing of pathogenic conflicts in the transference makes for greater therapeutic effectiveness. However, there has been a tendency to emphasize the genetic-historical interpretative approach to therapy at the expense of the role of the corrective emotional experience, i.e., the present as a reiteration of the past. If rigid, affective stereotypies are to be altered by employing historical interpretations in the present emotional context, the need for a certain repetitiveness, even of correct interpretations, is a necessary condition. Treatment itself is, after all, a part of present history.

The process of change in treatment includes an elaborate series of interactions between the treating person and patient. A great many of these must occur in the treatment situation itself, with both persons in the same physical setting. Such interactions alone, however, are insufficient for therapeutic change. It is also necessary for the patient to work over the experience at all levels of consciousness even when away from the treating person. Thus, some aspects of the process of change must occur relatively independently of the analyst or with the analyst in the role of another person, the transference figure. While many components of this process are immediately related to intellectual and verbal phenomena, much of the process is preconscious and nonverbal and highly affective in character. The effectiveness of the communicative work in treatment depends upon the actual hours spent with the patient and the reworking of the experience in both affective and ideational terms by the patient on his own. This process continues even when the latter is asleep. Much of what is considered working through in its proper sense is the time involved in actually experiencing and re-experiencing in intellectual as well as affective terms, so as to bring about constructive change. By its nature, this must occur both within the treatment sessions and outside of them.

In the same context the process of working through must continue after treatment itself has come to a successful conclusion. Maturity is not an end point but a continual process of growth. At most, a successful treatment eliminates earlier distortions of historical events and permits successful growth; in the process of treatment itself this has simply been given a good start. The period after the termination of treatment is not only one of reworking and re-experiencing life situations with greater facility and freedom, but also one of continuing to work through conflicts in new contexts and new situations.

The Contribution of Learning Theory

The more primitive aspects of human psychic functioning, based in the earlier history of the individual, are impressive both by their stereotypy and their affective character and, in the negative sense, by the relative absence of the higher intellectual processes. The frame of reference, if not the specific data of modern learning theory, throws some measure of light on these processes although it does not fully explain them. The factors of time, repetition, and reward, as related to the establishment of historical patterns of response and the assimilation of new experience, and the expression of such experience in terms of meaningful change is pertinent to the treatment process.

Emphasis upon the maturational aspects of human development has been translated into the technique of the insight-producing interpretation based in the prior history of the patient with resultant therapeutic change in behavior. As already discussed, when such change is delayed, it is assumed that the delay is due to the necessity for working through. An investigation of what happens in working through reveals many cue situations employed repetitively by the therapist. Now, through the years greater emphasis has been placed on the repetition of traumatic episodes in the past history of the patient as the source of neuroses rather than the impact of a single acute trauma. This principle has been advanced in connection with the "borderline states," though its more general implications have not been properly emphasized. Stern and more recently Brody have stressed this theme. In fact, the acute trauma has frequently represented a screen for earlier, often repetitive episodes of a different but related kind. Shakow[2] has stated this thesis most succinctly in the following terms:

I believe that because of many complex factors, we have unconsciously developed a certain theoretical bias—a bias which

[2] D. Shakow, "Research in Child Development: a Case Illustration of the Psychologist's Dilemma." Amer. J. Orthopsychiat. 22:45–59, 1959.

tends to emphasize the importance of the traumatic and the outstanding event, as opposed to the incidental, the casual, the undirected, and the unintended event; a bias which unduly emphasizes the single, isolated event, as opposed to the repetitive, the reiterated event. The traumatic and the isolated are almost without exception both more observable and reportable than are the incidental and the reiterated. We have tended to neglect on the one hand the important minimal events which are usually not reportable, and on the other the reiterated events which get missed because of their ubiquity. Is it for this reason that we have probed for and been more willing to accept memory images of such traumatic and isolated experiences as reasonably accurate representations of the actual events? In this respect Freud with his emphasis on trauma rather than Jones with his emphasis on habit has guided us. Footnote: In fairness to psychoanalysis, one should point out the emphasis which this system of psychology has placed on the trivial. But it must be remembered that what psychoanalysis emphasizes is the *present* trivial as a cue to the original or subsequent significant event. The point being made here is the *originally* minimal events are significant for development. (You remember James's "Every smallest stroke of virtue or of vice leaves its never so little scar." [*Principles of Psychology*, p. 127.] The respect which psychoanalytic ego psychology has developed for "automatization" is an important theoretical advance in the direction I am suggesting.

If it is true that in addition to acute and dramatic traumatic episodes, minimal, repeated, often unconscious or only partially perceived traumata are the substrate of neuroses, then it may well be that the opposite experience takes place during the therapeutic process. Attention has been centered on the acute and dramatic episodes; these are much more readily observable than the often subliminal therapeutic episodes. It becomes necessary now to explore the minimal cue situations and the less dramatic transactions between analyst and patient which supplement, but cannot replace, the genetic-historical exploration of emotional disorders. Just as repeated traumata rather than one single massive trauma are the historical source of the neuroses, the reverse sequence occurs during therapy despite the poignancy of the screen memory, the dramatic interpretation, and the occasional dramatic moment of change in therapy. The effectiveness of each of these is contingent on the painstaking preparatory groundwork, and each may be overvalued as being something more than a focus of crystallization. In therapy, repeated re-experiencing in dealing with anxiety-producing past experiences is a part of working through.

To what degree the necessary affective participation and abreaction in the therapeutic situation itself are dependent on cues which often are not identified by either partner is of course an open question. The available episodes in which some significant nonverbal cue on the patient's part is identified but which for technical reasons may or may not be communicated to him are numerous. A recent episode of this type concerned a patient who came into treatment with the conviction that he had a "poker face," and that if any of his associates said anything about what he might be experiencing internally this was not based upon any communication by him. One day he entered the office smiling, then stopped smiling and was silent. When asked what he was happy about, he responded with pleasant surprise to the therapist's identification of his feeling. When this was clarified, with acute affective participation on his part, he proceeded to describe the source of his pleasure. In this same context, the patient responds to many cues based upon the manner, bodily movements, etc., of the analyst as well.

Illustrations of Technique

With the background of the above considerations of affect and of working through, the technical approach to genetic–historical questions in treatment is more understandable and manageable. As was mentioned, in some obsessional patients who tend to isolate themselves from any affective participation in their reporting of prior events, it may be necessary to abandon the genetic–historical approach for extended periods of time. One resorts to exploring present events in the patient's life, both outside and within the treatment situation itself, in the interest of finding areas where the isolation of intellectual process and of affect may be less resistant. Only later may a return to the exploration of the prior experiences of the patient be carried out. Another frequently encountered technical problem in treatment occurs when the therapist may introduce historical information obtained from the patient in prior sessions. The possession of such information may be of value to the therapist but only rarely can he constructively volunteer such information in a therapeutic session. This is so because of the altered affective and ideational state of the patient making for a different mental set and mode of defense on his part. Historical material which was poignant and full of meaning for the patient at one time may be meaningless or heavily defended against by him at another. To illustrate:

A young woman twenty-five years old who was suffering from an hysterical phobic disorder, described during the course of a session a situation occurring at age nine when she and a boy her age had engaged in mutual examination of their genitalia. A somewhat modified version of this same incident in which she was the passive participant had been described by the patient six months previously and was remembered by the therapist but not mentioned or apparently remembered by the patient. It would not be therapeutically useful to interject this information since the patient has moved to another phase of development. The later and probably more accurate version of what "actually happened" was now the significant and affectively charged one, and the earlier version is irrelevant at the present moment in therapy.

This is in sharp distinction to the situation in therapy where the patient himself refers to some prior version of an historical event and seems to be struggling to correlate his own conscious and conflicting versions of prior events. In such circumstances the therapist may well choose to assist in exploring and correlating variable versions of historical events. This follows the general principle that the therapist take his leads from what the patient introduces and that he does not offer gratuitous information. Further illustrative of the same theme is a young man who reported that he had not fought with his parents until he was fifteen. Some weeks later he described stormy episodes with his parents at age five without mentioning the earlier version. For the therapist to choose gratuitously to recapitulate the prior event represents a technical error.

Depending on the level of resistance at a given time, historical data may be re-repressed. Thus, at a later time, the above patient reiterated the onset of overt conflict with his parents at age fifteen. A frontal assault on this repression would be futile. The therapeutic issue is one of exploring why the re-repression had occurred. Another instance of the re-repression of historical data is that of a young woman who reported with great guilt that she had, as a child, once taken some money from her mother's purse. At a later point where she was under considerable stress and experiencing the therapist in a different transference context, she entirely rejected the above bit of history and in complete candor stated that stealing was entirely alien to her nature and that she had never stolen anything in her entire life!

Of particular interest is the usual extensive to total amnesia experienced by persons who have undergone acute dissociative episodes, for instance an acute schizophrenic episode. These patients, on recovery, will experience even the most accurate historical account of their behavior or verbalization during such episodes as being alien to them. Attempts to offer them such data in the hope of reintegrating the fragmented segments of their personality are to no avail, and only those fragmented episodes recalled by the patient have therapeutic relevance. It is, in fact, a questionable hypothesis in persons with such serious ego defects as to whether the attempt to reconstruct a consistent and valid history with them is therapeutic.

There is, however, some correlation between the degree of integration or disorganization of the ego of the patient and the circumstances in which the therapist may choose to introduce historical data obtained from other informants or from the patient himself in the past. In the patient with a substantial degree of disorganization, the therapist is apt to function in the role of an accessory ego. In these circumstances and with the exception mentioned above, data obtained from others, from the patient himself, or from observations of the patient in the past may be introduced into the therapeutic situation. The therapist functions as part of the patient's memory and carries out part of his reality-testing function. In the better integrated patient, not only would it be undesirable for the therapist to invade the patient's autonomy but such an invasion would be responded to with well integrated defenses and would be to no avail.

Since there comes a time when the treatment process itself will become an historical event of the past, the question presents itself as to whether the accuracy of memory of the patient of his therapeutic experience has any correlation with the therapeutic result. Clinical experience would suggest that there is no significant direct correlation between the patient's capacity to formalize verbally his therapeutic experience and his degree of recovery. If anything, both a gross distortion of his experience and, at the opposite extreme, a too accurate reporting of the experience would suggest that the therapeutic result itself was a questionable one.

A phenomenon often commented upon having to do with history is that of a hiatus in the reported history—the several years in growing up when nothing is remembered, for instance. The general clinical impression is that this hiatus conceals historical events of especial significance. One might further speculate that such a hiatus represents an equivalent hiatus in the character structure. It is a deficit in the patient's curriculum vitae and in his integrative possibilities. This must be seen in relative terms, since even the healthy use only a limited part of their potential capabilities.

Memories of the Past and Internalizations as Constructive Forces

The function of the recalled past history of the patient as a force of considerable moment in determining his degree of integration and mood is considerable. How the patient sees his past affects his present living so much that it has been used as a technique of therapy in some situations. Viktor Frankl developed the intriguing idea that directing a patient's attention towards his curriculum vitae and towards the scope of his prior life events could serve as a useful antidote to the depression accompanying severe stress. As a concentration camp victim, he had found it to be a useful function in the dire stress of the camp situation, and he later used it with success in connection with persons suffering from incurable diseases and faced with death.

Memories of past events are an absolutely stable state in no one. There are normal fluctuations of such memories depending on the need for different modes of defense in different circumstances. Just so, the affective response to the memory of prior events is itself a variable at different points in time in the normal state. The pathogenicity of some memories of historical events resides in their lack of constructive integration into the character structure with the

103

accompanying pathogenic modes of defense against them. The present affective state of the patient influences how he will experience the recall of prior events and, reciprocally, his memories of prior experiences will influence his present affective state. The technical possibilities in connection with history and reconstructions offer an almost endless list, providing that a rational view of the historical and of the process of reconstruction and recall is taken.

It cannot be overstressed that the historically determined memories of the patient, including his automatic affective modes of response, derive from past experiences with actual persons. His perception of them and his later reworking of these perceptions result in certain internal images of those historical figures which become an integral part of his personality. Illustrative of this is the experience of mourning. In mourning, a host of memories of prior affective and ideational experiences are mobilized by the loss of another person who is then dealt with internally as if he were still alive. If the patient's image of this person changes, he will have changed himself, and this image rests not only in his intellect but in his affective attitude towards the internalized person. Needless to say his actual present physical existence is of little moment since the patient struggles, not with him, but with ghosts from the past.

VIII

THE ASSESSMENT OF INSANITY IN THE PAST

---···━▶◉◀━···---

Psychiatry and the Law

The purpose of this chapter is to demonstrate that, in certain circumstances, the evaluation of mental states at a time in the past is demanded of the psychiatrist and psychoanalyst. Many see the role of the courts as being alien and antithetical to their professional interests, but they are not infrequently involved in cases having to do with the courts and the law. The admission of the limitations of such reconstructive evaluations related to emotional disorders in the legal setting will throw further light on the involvement of the psychiatrist in the historical process. Certain aspects of the needs of the court will serve to illustrate the inevitability of the use of historical information in psychiatric expert opinion and will help to define the special characteristics of such information.

The global aspects of the legal concept of insanity has merited the attention of many brilliant legal and psychiatric scholars. There have been numerous proposed modifications of the legal concept of insanity. In criminal law, the problem of "right and wrong," irresistible impulse, and the various attempts at arriving at a working definition of insanity has been a concern of no small moment for both the law and psychiatry. One of the results of this interest has been the actual modification of the law itself as it relates to such matters, in some jurisdictions. Changes in the law or in the procedure of the

105

court have modified the very definitions of insanity itself in some instances, while in others the rules governing testimony by the psychiatrist have been modified. While all of this necessary concentration upon the general philosophy and actual practice of the law was going on, insufficient attention was directed towards specific areas of psychiatric-legal interaction. In addressing attention to a specific facet of the problem, it will be demonstrated that certain aspects of their potential collaboration will be brought into sharper focus. In this chapter, the specific issue of the determination of the existence of insanity at some point in the past in criminal actions is the area that has been chosen for examination, since this is a particular instance in which psychiatry and psychoanalysis are called upon to make such evaluations.

Insanity—as defined by the law—is subject to a variety of interpretations depending upon the given context in which it is being considered. Thus, the legal capacity to make a will, or testamentory capacity, is subject to laws which are quite different from those governing civil commitment to a mental institution and these, in turn, differ from the laws bearing on the ability to enter into a contract. The question of legal competence in criminal acts has markedly different legal significance than does the question of competence in other situations involving the courts. According to Professor Farinholt:

> Insanity is a legal term; it has no particular significance in medicine. In the law it has many different meanings depending upon the context in which the term is used. For example, "insanity" as it may affect testamentary capacity rests upon the finding of a mental condition which would prevent the testator at the time of making his will from having "a full understanding of the nature of the business in which he was engaged; a recollection of the property of which he intended to dispose and the persons to whom he meant to give it, and the relative claims of the different persons who were or should have been the objects of his bounty." This, of course, differs markedly from the meaning of so-called "insanity" in criminal proceedings.[1]

[1] Prof. L. Whiting Farinholt, University of Maryland School of Law, personal communication.

Psychiatry is called upon by criminal law to offer opinions on three disparate concepts of insanity. The first of these is whether or not a state of insanity exists in the present. This is based on judgments of whether the accused can communicate with his attorney and participate in his own defense. The second is whether the accused was insane at the time of the offense and so should not be held responsible. This is based upon the definition of legal responsibility as exercised in the given jurisdiction. It rests upon the M'Naghten Rule, the "irresistible impulse" concept, the Durham Rule, the Model Penal Code, or some variation of these. The third is whether the accused is insane in the sense that he is dangerous to himself or others and should accordingly be confined in a mental institution until it is felt that such dangers are no longer present. This latter is the basis for usual commitment procedures. As may be noted, both the issues at stake and the very definition of insanity itself are different in the three situations mentioned above. The present focus is on the question of whether insanity existed at the time of a crime in the past, since this will throw light on the strengths and limitations of psychiatry as an evaluative instrument in questions of criminal responsibility and thus on this particular facet of historical reconstruction.

History and the Law

Typical examples of this use of history are the following actual cases:

A forty-one-year-old father of eleven children set fire to his house in December, 1964. This act resulted in the death of seven of his children. He was separated from his wife and family at the time. He was tried on the last day of February, 1967. It was the court's decision, based on psychiatric testimony, that he was presently sane (i.e., capable of standing trial), but was insane (i.e., not legally responsible) at the time that he set the fire. As a consequence, he was found innocent by reason of insanity. At the time that the fire was set, this man was on bail on a prior charge of second-degree murder and is currently serving an eighteen-year sentence for it. A man who accompanied him during the fire-setting was sentenced to life imprisonment in February, 1966, on that charge.

Another case decided by the same court on the same day was that of a man accused of fatally shooting and killing a young woman (aged twenty-three), and an off-duty policeman. He was found to be presently sane (i.e., capable of standing trial), but insane (i.e., not legally responsible) at the time of the shootings. He was committed to a state mental hospital for the criminally insane "for further observation and treatment." In the state in which these events occurred, if a man is found to be insane (i.e., not legally responsible) at the time of an alleged crime although presently sane (i.e., capable of standing trial), he is remanded to a psychiatric hospital. In such time as the hospital may feel that this person is capable of resuming his place in the community it will sue the court for permission to return him to the community, and the nature of his prior involvement in the alleged crime is not legally relevant.

In psychiatric practice the appraisal by the psychiatrist of whether an individual is or is not psychotic is based upon the psychiatric history, the psychiatric examination of the patient, psychological examination, physical and neurological examination, and such additional tests of a physical nature as may be indicated, such as electroencephalographic studies, etc. Of these, by far the most significant part of the examination is the psychiatric examination of the patient by the psychiatrist himself. In the psychiatric examination the appearance, mode of behavior, mode of speech, kinds of feelings he reports experiencing (or seems to be experiencing as evidenced by his manifest behavior), the actual content and level of organization of his speech, evidences of delusions or hallucinations, capacity to carry out simple tests of mental functioning, and his general outlook on life, moral sense, and ability to make reasonable judgments, are taken as a measure of whether or not the patient can be looked upon as a responsible individual or whether his functioning is impaired to a degree where it is felt that he represents a gross danger to himself or others.

As may be seen, the determination of whether or not a person is a responsible agent in this particular context is fraught with great difficulty and is at best a skilled opinion. It cannot be said to have the relatively absolute quality of a truly scientific opinion. Science rests upon the possibilities of quantification and the possibilities of drawing conclusions based upon the examination of similar instances by the use of statistical methods. In the individual instances in which the law is interested, such as the state of mind of one given person at some point in time, scientific methodology is of very limited value. It can point general directions but cannot give the specific answer the court so sorely needs. Psychiatry and psychoanalysis cannot offer precise, quantitative answers which can be experimentally validated. Furthermore, there is no reason to believe that the behavioral sciences will be of significant help in the future in answering the kind of question which is the subject of this chapter.

Not only is there considerable confusion about the meaning of the term *insane* in the legal sense, but there is great confusion about the commonly used analogous psychiatric term *psychosis* in psychiatric circles. Since in psychiatric terms generally there is not felt to be any sharp line of division between the so-called neuroses and the psychoses, and since there are persons who may shift from one state to another and the reverse, there seems to be little of definite descriptive value in these terms, for legal purposes at least. Even in psychiatric terms the word psychosis is fraught with confusion. Thus, while the psychoses are felt to be disorders of greater severity as marked by greater disturbance of contact with reality and with greater chronicity, these things are not regularly the case. Many non-psychotic mental disorders are of great chronicity and may be marked by considerable disturbance in appraisals of reality. Of course, in the grossest instances there is no reasonable likelihood of confusion since the blatant psychoses in some instances show the most severe disturbance of capacity to appraise reality. In others, however, as in the paranoid psychoses except for certain discrete areas, reality testing may be relatively unimpaired. More than a few psychiatric authorities have responded to the confusion invoked by the terms neurosis and psychosis by recommending that the terms be dropped altogether for psychiatric purposes. Of course, for legal purposes some manner of distinction must be made between those who may be considered to be responsibly charged for their behavior and those who should be exempt on the grounds that their behavioral performances are beyond their control.

Considering the not infrequent circumstances in which it is difficult to establish whether the patient is psychotic in the present, the issue becomes even more obscure when the psychiatrist is asked to offer an opinion about the presence or absence of psychosis at some prior point in time many months before the time of his actual examination. This is the state of affairs when the psychiatrist in a criminal case is asked for his opinion about the mental state of the accused in the present, to which he is entitled to give an expert opinion, and at some point in the past when the accused is alleged to have committed a crime, often of very great seriousness. At most this latter is little more than an "educated guess." The fact that the court asks the psychiatrist for such an opinion and the fact that many psychiatrists have seen fit to offer an authoritative opinion about the question of the presence or absence of insanity at some point in the past does not in itself argue for the validity of such opinions since such precedents may rest upon mutual folly. This is so since it is not generally possible on the basis of prior history to establish whether or not a state of insanity existed in the past. The exceptions to this, of course, are based on the results of expert examinations at, or immediately after, the alleged criminal act. As is true in legal circles, data obtained by the psychiatrist from the patient as to his actual verbal productions and his actual behavior at the time of examination have much the higher level of credibility. Hearsay has questionable virtues.

The kinds of data which the psychiatrist can obtain from the patient himself and upon which he then bases his opinion are much the strongest. However, whether or not the psychiatrist is of the opinion that the patient is sane or insane at the present point in time, extrapolations to the state of the patient at some prior point in time are always precarious. Such opinions are, at best, based upon reported aberrations of behavior at some past point and reported data about the patient's thinking and feeling at these prior points. As might be surmised, such reports, and particularly so in the stress of the situation involving the accused, are of limited credibility. This is a particularly difficult problem since the psychiatrist is being asked to offer an opinion about the mental state of the accused at a time in the past when he was said to have carried out a behavioral performance which grossly violates usual community standards. There are those who are of the opinion that the capacity to carry out acts—for instance, of violence or murder—would in itself suggest serious mental abnormality. However, this has hardly been the opinion of the psychiatric community at large.

Nevertheless a not insignificant amount of the opinion of whether or not a given person was insane at the time of an alleged crime tends to be based on his actual behavioral performance at the time: on whether or not this was a particularly exotic crime, whether the alleged criminal seemed to be controlled by rational impulses, etc. As may be seen, this point of view places the psychiatrist in the role of judging whether or not the crime actually occurred in the described manner and whether the accused did in fact commit it. This is particularly so in pre-trial investigations. In this position the psychiatrist is much in the role of the judge and jury itself. The courts have taken a dim view of the use of such tenuous evidence in the conduct of their own affairs and yet they seem to place considerable validity on opinions of the psychiatrist based on such evidence simply because they themselves have declared him an expert.

The Basis for the Psychiatrist's Expert Opinion

In the usual case, the psychiatrist asked to give opinions as an expert witness must base such opinions solely upon information presented to the jury through the lips of witnesses having first-hand knowledge. An opinion is inadmissible if premised upon information from third parties who have merely reported their information about the facts in issue to the psychiatrist out of court, as is the case in respect to a case history which the psychiatrist has acquired from fellow staff members at an institution, nurses' notes, etc. In actual practice, such out-of-court information is frequently used by the psychiatrist in forming his opinion, and the court either admits the opinion without requiring additional proof by relaxing its rules or the psychiatrist *claims* that his opinion is based upon his own observation and that ancillary sources of information did not influence his opinion.

It is not an infrequent event for a mental illness to follow an irregular course so that during the process of such an illness there may be occasions when a person may be said to be "insane," interspersed with other occasions when he is "sane." This statement can be made with authority since in the longitudinal study of mental illness this is a common finding. Furthermore, fluctuations

111

between states of sanity and insanity are not generally limited to any given psychiatric diagnostic category. This may be the source of confusion since, in some situations including ones involving the courts, predictive statements about the course of mental illness can be made by the psychiatrist with reasonable certainty. This is so, for example, in divorce proceedings which rest upon the question of whether a marital partner is presently mentally ill and will probably remain so in the future. The psychiatrist takes the position that the chronicity of the illness, its nature, and the present findings on psychiatric examination of the patient allow him a reasonable estimate of the future course of the illness. This opinion is based on the opportunity to examine the patient in the present, and no opinion would be acceptable which did not include such an examination. Even such predictions are sometimes false although made by psychiatrists of the highest skills.

In offering an estimate of the insanity of the accused at the time of a past crime, the psychiatrist as expert is doing no more than offering his "best guess." It is likely that his surmise will be more accurate than that of the average untrained person, although this would not lend itself to absolute proof. The issue is further complicated by the fact that the psychiatrist draws heavily on his intuitive sense of the probable state of affairs in the past. Thus he depends on the data available to him and on his own responses to the accused in coming to a decision. For purposes of exposition, he may bolster his intuitive sense with rational argument and it is this latter which is offered to the court and subject to cross-examination. The psychiatrist's role as an intuitive instrument does not lend itself to legal process, and yet it is at the heart of his "best guess."

It is important to be entirely clear about the limits of the diagnostic capabilities of psychiatry and especially so in those psychiatric disorders which may be due to organic causes. Even the so-called functional psychoses are not exempt since many of them may well turn out, in the future, to have organic as well as psychogenic etiology. For instance, schizophrenia is probably a potpourri of disorders bearing some superficial resemblances which, likely as not, derive from a variety of causative factors. The span of these may well stretch all the way from specifically physical organic difficulties to the impact of poor upbringing. Historically the states now called schizophrenia were called *de-*

mentia praecox and, as the name *dementia praecox* itself suggests, it was said to begin in the young. The very diagnosis itself inferred that it followed a progressively deteriorating course. In the event that someone so designated did recover, the very fact of recovery warranted changing the diagnosis. The introduction of the term schizophrenia was made, among other reasons, for the very purpose of removing the prognosis as being a central factor in the diagnosis. Many people diagnosed as having schizophrenia at present do indeed recover, and a significant number of them never have another psychotic episode. Since psychiatry derives from the medical disciplines and since it is associated in the public's mind with them, there has been the tendency to view diagnostic categories as having the same validity as they do in the organic disease states. Organic medicine, while it is still considerably an art, has made strides in the direction of establishing itself as a scientific discipline. At least presently, and perhaps permanently, the scientific development of medicine far transcends the development of a true science in psychiatry.

Psychiatry and the principles underlying human behavior which derive from it have supplied many illuminating insights which help in the understanding of normal, abnormal, and even criminal behavior. These insights have had a powerful impact on the attitudes towards deviant behavior in our culture: for example, the shifting attitudes towards rehabilitation as opposed to punishment in dealing with the criminal. When the point at issue is more specific however, such as the presence or absence of insanity at some point in time, psychodynamic principles are of no significant help. These principles are relevant to inner states of conflict and to the balance between the various forces making up the character. They are not good predictive instruments, in themselves, of behavioral patterns. The least accurate aspect of such dynamic principles is the estimate of the relative strength of the conflicting forces. In fact, behavior itself is used as one frame of reference which is employed in the attempt to quantitate the relative strength of these forces making up the character. Thus, in a patient with explosive behavior, the psychiatrist might then attempt to ascertain whether this derives from an excessive strength of the drives or a weakness of the ego. The behavioral pattern is often the clue to the existence of an imbalance within the personality structure, and from this a quantitative factor is inferred.

Psychic Equivalent States

Perhaps the most tantalizing group of psychiatric disorders as they relate to criminal acts are those of psychomotor epilepsy or, as they are sometimes called, psychic equivalent states. The very obscurity of these behavioral disorders has made for a situation where they lend themselves particularly well to usage as a defense in criminal cases. As the name infers, these states are a substitutive form of epilepsy. Epilepsy itself is defined as a disorder in which there is a disturbance of the electro-physico-chemical activity of the brain. It is evidenced by: (a) changes in the electrical production of the brain (b) a variety of disturbances of consciousness (c) in some persons by a convulsive seizure and in others by psychic states of various sorts, from fear to rage and behavioral disturbances. The latter are highly variable in character and include such disparate patterns as "running fits" and homicidal outbursts. Attacks of epilepsy may or may not be preceded by a warning signal in the way of specific behavioral patterns or seeing lights, etc. prior to the onset of the attack itself. Attacks may be set off by a great variety of sights, sounds, smells, or even by anxiety itself.

Of special interest is the epileptic equivalent state in which, as was mentioned, homicidal attacks may be made. The epileptic equivalent state is marked by trancelike states and confusional episodes which are commonly of brief duration. The patient is usually amnesic for such episodes after the attack. During the attack itself the patient may have delusional thoughts and auditory or visual hallucinations. In some persons suffering from psychomotor epilepsy there may be electroencephalographic findings. When present they are to be found in the anterior pole of the temporal lobe of the brain. The findings themselves are by no means diagnostic although there tends to be some suggested regularity in the pattern of electroencephalographic change. The mood in epileptic equivalent states may vary from alarm to terror, to irritability, to rage, to depression, to confusion, to bewilderment and may eventuate in outbursts of rage. In them the patient may be suicidal or homicidal. Although in some instances his behavior may be of extreme violence and appear apparently senseless, in others he may show *apparent* discrimination and judgment although he is quite incapable of controlling his behavioral performances. Such states may last from minutes to hours, or days. Although consciousness may be preserved, there may be complete or partial amnesia for the episode itself. On occasion trance-like or dream-like states may be experienced. The patient is in effect denied access to his own history.

In view of the broad range of possible causes for episodes of violent behavior, ranging all the way from episodic outbursts in the schizophrenic to outbursts following upon major epileptic seizures, there are apt to be sharp differences of opinion among psychiatrists on any given patient as to his diagnosis even when no forensic matter is at issue. Particularly in the gray area of psychomotor epilepsy is our knowledge so limited that it is not possible to make a truly definite diagnosis in many instances. The limited credibility of expert opinion in such instances should not be concealed since otherwise the court is misinformed as to the "scientific" nature of the opinion being offered.

The Credibility of Psychiatric Opinions

As opposed to any ordinary witness who testifies only as to facts, the expert witness testifies as to facts and opinions based upon these facts. The need for the court to use expert witnesses is above question. The opinion of a man who is knowledgeable in a given area, when based upon his interpretation of the available data, will be more accurate than that which could be drawn by an ordinary layman or even the court itself. The dilemma arises when, having established a given person as being expert in a certain area, the court is no longer able to discriminate the level of credibility of the inferences the expert may make. There are safeguards in the legal process in that opposing experts may be called to neutralize or discredit inferences of doubtful credibility. In addition, the expert himself may be exposed to cross-examination. In all such situations, however, the courts are in the unenviable position of having to evaluate the opinions of opposing experts on technical matters in which they can have only a very limited discriminatory capacity. In the cross-examination itself, not only are the opinions of the expert under scrutiny, but his capacity to cope with the structure of legal procedure is being measured. As a consequence the courts are vulnerable to the persuasive capacities of some experts rather than to the validity of their scientific opinions. Just so, the courts are vulnerable to the skill of the opposing side in presenting its case and in cross-examination. These problems are particularly apt to be true in medico-psychiatric matters when the issue itself is obscure as is the case in many situations involving competency.

Objections have been raised that conflicting testimony of experts is not of such a nature as to allow the courts to be able to come to resolutions of their difficulties. There are those who have suggested that this question might be resolved by procedural modifications by means of which the experts might consult and arrive at a consensus which would then be offered to the court. The validity of such a procedure must rest, however, on the absolute nature of the subject under inquiry and the capacity of the expert to form incontrovertible opinions. Thus, in a manifest fracture of the femur there would be absolute consensus among the experts. In psychiatry, however, the data available leaves the widest room for the biases of the expert to exert influence. This derives from the relatively non-specific nature of psychiatric data. Experts—particularly in psychiatry and psychoanalysis—supply a point of view which is of value, but it is rarely a "neutral" opinion. The biases of the physician and psychiatrist, of both a social and professional nature, are to some degree manifest in their expert testimony. The more equivocal the illness the more will the bias of the examiner become evident. In equivocal situations an expert's bias is often so evident that one could, with some accuracy, predict apparently irrelevant data about him based on his opinion in an ostensibly medical matter. Such predictions might include his probable voting habits, his attitude toward social issues, etc. The bias of the expert in psychiatry may be expressed even in the diagnostic term chosen by him. Thus the diagnostic term "psychopathic personality" carries with it a negative connotation and is used by many to connote badness rather than sickness. Another psychiatrist might diagnose the same person as suffering from a "character disorder" with the reverse connotation. In general, the more fully acquainted the psychiatrist becomes with a given person the more apt is he to see him as sick rather than bad.

Given that the expert testimony available is no more than as above stated, it would be unfortunate for the court to relinquish its right to come to a common sense, best guess as to which testimony to consider most credible. Unless it could be clearly demonstrated that a consensus among experts rests on matters other than who is the dominant person among the group of experts, whether they share common biases on social issues, etc., then the court would be ill-advised to give up its prerogatives. It would have to be demonstrated that the opinion of the group of experts is based on more objective findings than are generally available in the many equivocal situations in psychiatry. The limited capability of the court to discriminate can hardly be used as an argument to turn over such discrimination to others unless it could be demonstrated that these others have a far greater capacity to discriminate.

While procedural changes which would allow the psychiatrist to tell more freely the facts and conjectures upon which he bases his opinion are of some value, there is great danger of overevaluating their accuracy when the particular situation is that of estimating the presence or absence of psychosis in the past in a person now felt to be sane. Dynamic psychiatry deals largely with the inner world of man and the world of man's impulses and desires bears no one-to-one relationship with the world of his acts. Thus, for instance, based upon estimates of the world of man's inner experience there has been a long-standing popular myth that criminals are frequently in the habit of returning to the scene of their crime. As a practical matter this is an occurrence of the greatest rarity.

Responsibility For Past Acts

Whenever the question of the validation of actual events in the past is at issue, the capacity of man to choose—determinism vs. free-will—seems to intrude itself. The law, with its social orientation, bases its very decision as to guilt or innocence on the premise that man is capable of choosing what his behavior will be when he is in the normal state. Psychiatry and psychoanalysis have tended to vacillate, since, while they are heavily deterministic in orientation, they postulate that treatment itself will strengthen the ego and, with it, permit a broader span of choice of behavior. As was mentioned earlier in this volume, Berlin's common sense view of free will as an inevitable trait of psychic organization is accepted, along with those aspects of man's behavior which are the product of factors outside of his area of choice. Viewed in this way, the conclusion may be reached that, to a significant degree, man can make his own history if free of the bonds of neuroticism and overwhelming social pressures.

The law itself recognizes many extenuating circumstances in its judgment of the capacity to exercise free will. Thus, the question of the age of the accused, whether or not the crime was done in the "heat of passion," whether it was done in self defense, etc., are taken into consideration as factors which would reduce the capacity to make free choice. Just so, the laws governing insanity in criminal acts are addressed to the same questions. In these circumstances even the law itself states that a man is not the master of his own acts and his own historical creations. He is a slave of forces beyond his control and is a passive spectator at the creation of his own history.

In the context of the historical process, the law poses many puzzling problems to the psychiatrist. The law is not unacquainted with the complexity of establishing matters of fact related to events of the past. It employs a sieve through which the data brought to it are exposed. The sieve consists of common sense and a traditional set of rules. If data pass through it, it is dealt with as being "true." This heuristic approach to establishing the validity of past historical events differs from the positive approach to establishing historical events. The limits of the positive approach available to the psychiatrist in predicting mental states in the past bears on the subject of his capacity to reconstruct history. In the particular context of the law and of the need to establish what "actually happened" he is of limited value. As will be developed, his use of reconstructions of history are of great value only in the sphere of assisting the patient to alter his inner view of the world. Secondarily, the patient's behavior in the future may then be affected.

IX

THE SENSE OF REALITY AND VALUES OF THE ANALYST AS HISTORIAN *

The Framework in Which the Analyst Functions

Little direct attention has been addressed to the question of the psychoanalyst's use of his own appraisal of reality and his own values as a regular and necessary part of the taking of a history, the examination of a patient, or the treatment process itself. Values cannot be expected to arise from psychiatric or psychoanalytic knowledge and no "natural" hierarchy of values exists which is universally valid. Values, and in fact the way we see the world, aside from the distortions of neurosis, are significantly determined by our extra-analytic appraisal of the social structure. These themes have been elucidated in connection with the explorations of psychiatry and of psychoanalysis into related fields such as education, but their immediate relevance to the actual work needs further development. Appraisals of reality and value appraisals on the therapist's part are influenced by his training but they basically derive from the vicissitudes of his own genetic and developmental experiences. Without a

* At the time of his death Dr. Novey was revising this chapter to suit the purposes of this book, which are not confined to psychoanalysis alone. Because he did not complete his revisions, it has been thought best to reprint this chapter almost exactly as it appeared in the International Journal of Psycho-Analysis. It is clear, however, that much of what he says here about psychoanalysis is meant to refer to dynamic psychotherapy as well.—R.N.

119

fortuitous combination of both of these circumstances he could neither assume the posture which is necessary in order for him to do his job nor could he actually ever take a valid history or make a valid interpretation.

There are self-evident dangers in an intrusive valuative position on the analyst's part which can disrupt therapy, and for this reason among others, the "gray-screen position" of the analyst came into being. This position represents a useful model, but it can be overdrawn. The objection to too puristic a view in no sense negates the need for the therapist to develop and to maintain a high degree of awareness of his own drives and psychological dynamics such as to permit him to avoid interacting with the patient in a fashion which would falsify the data obtained from the patient and stabilize or intensify the patient's neurotic modalities. In other words, he must not fall into the error of co-operating with the patient in his repetitive neurotic mode of seeing the world and of behaving under the guise of "interpreting reality" to him. These requirements of the analyst are in the interest of maintaining himself as an objective although involved participant in the diagnostic and treatment processes. Such objectivity is looked upon as the opposite of the countertransference attitude, if the term countertransference is used to designate unconscious neurotic attitudes of the therapist manifesting themselves in the therapeutic setting. Objectivity infers the capacity to "see the patient for what he is" and to sort out a "reality picture" from the welter of conflicting reports about himself or others. In addition, it implies his ability to maintain a realistic view of himself and his own motivations. This is the necessary substrate upon which the process of ascertaining the inner play of the patient's conflicting forces and emotions can be carried out.

Reality Testing—the Sense of Reality—and Values

For the present purposes, external reality will simply be used to imply that a common consensus could be established within a specific culture that a given event or situation has or has not transpired. This definition is suggested in full awareness that it hardly takes care of all of the niceties but is sufficient for the present purpose. It is essential to differentiate the capacity to appraise external reality, a characteristic of the ego's function of reality testing, from the "sense of reality" as defined by Federn. In reality testing the ego calls upon its perceptual ability continuously to probe the environment by means of sensory modalities and to collate this information with its stored memories as a means of preparation for dealing with the environment. The "sense of reality," on the other hand, has to do with the inner experience of the self and the world as a cohesive unit having existence. Usually, there is no particular self-consciousness as to the intactness of oneself or the external world. This faculty is disturbed and becomes conspicuous in such states as depersonalization and derealization. While no sharp line of division can be drawn between those aspects of reality testing dependent on stored memories and the special series of affectively laden memories constituting the sense of values, the latter is specifically delineated. The sense of values is meant to infer a body of judgments, deriving from the conscious and unconscious attitudes of the parents primarily, as representative of society, structurally representing a part of both ego and superego and intended to represent guides in behavior.

While the psychoanalyst's primary concern is with the imbalance between the various forces within the personality, and structurally with the imbalance between id, ego, and superego, a not inconsiderable part of these structures themselves, derives from the incorporation of the environment as represented by the parents or others. This is so in addition to the particular contributions of the individual himself in the way of inborn characteristics, idiosyncratic modes and types of incorporation and identification. There is generally a relatively high degree of concurrence between the value systems of the analyst and analysand, derived as they are prone to be, from the same broad culture. This makes both for greater understanding and empathy and also for certain general principles of conduct which can be "taken for granted." Since, in the neuroses at least, the patient is apt to suffer from an overly severe and even cruel superego, the psychotherapist or psychoanalyst is apt to find himself more often than not in an allegiance with the patient against it, and thus fails to identify his own role as including any particular value system.

It is likely that less exception would be taken to the use of the therapist's ability to test reality than in the more specific sphere of his sense of values. While there is ample reason to caution against the imposition of his values and prejudices upon the patient, there are certain limits beyond which this cannot be held to be applicable. There is a common means of skirting this issue by making the assumption that socially reasonable behavior is itself a mark of mental health and that all asocial and antisocial behavior is by that fact neurotic. This is hardly a tenable position, but if accepted it places the psychotherapist or psychoanalyst in the role of defining mental health in purely social terms rather than in terms of the interplay of forces within the individual, a position which has been vigorously opposed by some. Yet, to use a gross example, it would be a rare psychotherapist or psychoanalyst indeed who could accept the notion that a bank robber could be making use of his creativity and sublimatory abilities in such a fashion that they would not be looked upon as symptomatic of neurosis, however successful he might be at his chosen occupation. Given that there are certain universal taboos such as those against incest and murder, there is a broad group of behavioral performances where his judgment does come into play. He may employ standards somewhat at variance with the "official" views of the society itself but he is, by his nature, a product of his culture and subject to its system of values.

As regards the analyst's reality testing, for the most part the lack of attention to it derives from the fact that his appraisal of reality has been accepted as a necessary condition for the appraisal of the patient and for treatment, and the tendency has been to accept it in absolute terms without question. The model for which he strives is one in which his own primary processes do not intrude themselves into the preliminary appraisal or the therapeutic situation—that he be governed by his own secondary process in dealing with the patient and that, optimally, all of his dealings with the patient be within the sphere of his consciousness. This asks for a constant "free floating" attention to his own preconscious process as well as the equally necessary attention to what may be going on within the patient. Insofar as the psychoanalyst may deviate from an accurate appraisal of the patient's psychic state given appropriate time and possibilities for inquiry, he engages in some manner of neurotic interaction which is deleterious to the patient. One of the several definitions of countertransference is based upon this thesis and of course this most common definition of the term carries a negative

122

connotation. Since it is not possible or desirable to perceive of the patient *in vacuo*, another tacit assumption is that the patient is appraised within a certain social situation, and this is at least one of the functions of the initial history and its later elaboration. In addition to an appraisal of inner conflict, it is necessary to ascertain how external reality impinges upon him, what influence it has upon his inner conflicts, what defenses he employs, and so on. Pursuant to this his subsequent modes of attempting to deal with external reality are a matter of interest both in themselves and insofar as they may throw light on his psychic processes.

In connection with this, the term "average expectable environment" has come increasingly into common parlance in psychoanalytic circles as has the term "average expectable internal conflicts." The usage of such terms as "average expectable" implies appraisal by the therapist of the culture as well as of the patient's conflicts and of the need on his part to take some valuative position about both of them. While the term *average expectable behavior* is not used, it would seem to be a natural consequence of the mode in which the patient deals with his conflicts in what is adjudged to be an "average expectable environment" or an "average not-expectable environment," i.e., what is judged to be a typical or an atypical situation. This seems to be one of a kind with Hartmann's use of the term "adaptive behavior." He suggests that this term has greater biological significance than the term "reality syntonic" in that the latter over-estimates the importance of understanding rather than of action, and adaptive behavior is oriented towards action or preparation for action or the inhibition of action. It transcends simply thinking or knowing. To use the old psychological terminology, it is a blend of affect, conation, and cognition without giving absolute primacy to any of them, but with cognition as the organizer. While the dominance of cognition is open to question, it will not be elaborated upon further here.

Clinical Examples of the Use of Reality and Value Judgments

The therapist's appraisal of the patient in an environment is thus included as a part of the total psychotherapeutic or psychoanalytic situation. Depending upon the relative degree of ability to conduct such appraisals on the patient's part it is used, if not to communicate to the patient directly, at least to maintain the therapist's orientation so that he may carry out his stated task. For purposes of illustration a gross example of this, from a more profound mental disorder, occurs when the analyst concludes that the patient is having auditory hallucinations. This conclusion depends on the verbal statement of the patient, or a certain suggestive behavioral pattern of the patient, that he is hearing voices when such voices *are not audible to the analyst.* In this instance he employs his own sensory experiences—or lack of them—to validate or invalidate the reality or actuality of the event reported by the patient. This is not to say that the patient is not having the stated experience or that this is not a matter of great relevance in the examination or treatment situation itself, but it does say that in his judgment the patient's experience is not coincident with external reality. As might be expected, it is just here—when he has to do with the psychoses—that the psychoanalyst most clearly perceives the need to function as an accessory ego for the patient. The fact is that there is no sharp cut-off point between the psychoses and the neuroses and particularly so in the necessarily regressed states which are a common part of psychotherapy and of psychoanalysis, however much such regression may be "in the service of the ego" in these circumstances.

In a gross instance such as the above, the issue is a relatively clear one; however, there are all sorts of gradations from the gross example cited to the minute and subtle judgments he is called upon to make during the process of diagnosis and treatment. Such judgments as to the relative degree of external reality in the data reported by the patient are often the substrate upon which interventions are based. For instance, the estimate by the analyst of the character of a marital partner—as reported by the patient—will inevitably play a role in his appraisal of and eventually in the direction of the interpretations offered to the patient. This applies not only to current figures, of course, but also to prior significant persons in the patient's life.

The objection might perhaps be raised that the analyst is not called upon to make such judgments and that the use of them would in fact be intrusive. A series of illustrations from the recent literature would seem to suggest the legitimacy and in fact the inevitability of such appraisals by him.

Greenacre refers to the bizarreness and improbability of a memory in the following context.

A woman patient had a screen memory that as a child she had been punished by being aroused from sleep at night, brought downstairs, forced to kneel before a punishment chair and to eat asparagus from a platter placed in the seat of the chair. What was striking was not only the *bizarreness of this improbable memory* [italics by author], but the patient's complete conviction that it had occurred exactly as she related it. This screen memory was a remarkable piece of condensation, involving several experiences in reality, and was based on the patient's observations of sexual activities between her mother and her psychotic father; and her own re-enactment of these with cousins. Her insistence on the reality of the memory not only bore testimony to the reality of the experiences, but may have been the greater because of her guilty terror of having behaved in a crazy fashion like her father.[1]

Gitelson refers to a man's qualifications for a given task:

Some years ago I was analyzing a schizoid patient. The analysis was progressing favorably when, at the end of about a year, the patient was faced with the prospect of making a public appearance *in a capacity for which he was well qualified.*[2] [Italics by author.]

Fliess refers to a specific characteristic of the analyst himself. In an illustration of the representation of the whole through a part of an object he uses an example where even the part is seen incorrectly:

A patient in the beginning of his analysis commented frequently on the blue color of my eyes. [*My eyes are not blue but a distinct gray*—Fliess.][3]

---

[1] Phyllis Greenacre, "Re-evaluation of the Process of Working Through," *Int. J. Psychoanal.* 33:6, 1952.

[2] Maxwell Gitelson, "The Emotional Position of the Analyst in the Psychoanalytic Situation," *Int. J. Psychoanal.* 33: 6, 1952.

[3] Robert Fliess, "On the Nature of Human Thought," in *Readings in Psychoanalytic Psychology*, ed. *Morton Levitt* (New York: Appleton-Century-Crofts, Inc., 1959).

An example that came from a colleague is the following, representative of the need to use the therapist's reality testing as a mode of validation of historical data by the rules of simple probability. Thus a young man reported that he had left an excellent college in the freshman year since he could not work and that his working capacity had "fallen apart" three years ago, at the time of the death of his father. Since in these times, both good grades and stringent entrance examinations are requisites for entrance to this college [*as was well known to the psychiatrist*] it seemed improbable that the reduction of functional capacity as described by the patient could be accurate.

Glover[4] discusses at some length the technical question of how to deal with matters introduced by the patient which are felt to be "real" by the analyst in the particular sphere of criticisms made by the patient about him. He states this in such attractive and humorous terms that it fully warrants being quoted in its entirety:

Here we must pause to consider an issue of some importance. I have said that the patient's criticisms should be sampled by the analyst's reality ego, and in many instances the patient's projections or infantile identifications of the analyst with parental figures are easy to detect. The patient may with every accent of sincerity characterize him as a low and ignorant fellow, a boor and a philistine, his mother probably a washerwoman of dubious moral habits, his wife socially impossible, his offspring mentally or physically defective, his wall-paper a scream, his analysis incompetent, his aspect repulsive or obscene. The more skilled the patient's tongue the more delicate will these and innumerable other innuendoes become; and in the nature of things many of his more sophisticated shafts will reach the mark. In this case the analyst will be faced with alternative policies. Recognizing the projective or transference origin of the attack, he may disregard the validity of the criticisms, treating these as no more important than the reality element of a rationalization, and proceed to interpret the patient's reactions in terms of their infantile background. By so doing he tacitly denies any validity whatsoever to the patient's animadversions. Or, on the other hand, he may freely grant the

---

[4] Edward Glover, *The Technique of Psychoanalysis* (New York: International Universities Press, 1955), pp. 103–4.

validity of such criticisms *as he recognizes to be well founded.*
[Italics by author.] A simple illustration would be where a
patient, suffering from a guilt reaction, is in the habit of maintaining that the analyst is irritable with him. But what if on
some occasions the analyst is for some reason or other actually
irritable. Should he nevertheless blandly continue to analyze
the patient's projection or should he admit that the criticism is
on this occasion just?

Now although common sense would dictate the obvious
course of disclaiming any perfectionist attributes, there is no
doubt that the one-sided situation of analysis allows the analyst
considerable scope to evade any reality reactions he may have
by concentrating somewhat tendentiously on the analysis of the
patient. He can always maintain that if a patient remarks "you
have a hole in your sock," the actual existence of a hole is not
so important, as the fact that the patient has a hostile or projective or symbolic reason for calling attention to the fact. And
he can if he wishes ask the obvious analytic question "what
does the idea of a hole in *my* sock bring to *your* mind?" [Italics
by Dr. Glover.] If, however, he sticks to this policy, he must
put up with the consequence of implying tacitly that he is without flaw: for in that case the patient's super-ego transferences
will never be fully resolved. It is a better long-term policy for
the analyst never to deny the validity of a well-founded criticism, and to allow a certain margin for blind spots to his own
defects. He will thereby have much more freedom to return
to the analysis of his patient's projection.

It should be noted that Glover is writing about the particular
sphere where, hopefully, the analyst would be best equipped to
make judgments, namely in comments about himself. Frequently,
as the other writers previously quoted suggest, the analyst is called
upon to pass judgment on persons and situations in which he is not
himself directly participant.

Hartmann[5] discussed the issue of the psychotherapist's appraisal
of reality in a more theoretical framework when he refers to the
therapist's need to evaluate the origins of guilt as a regular and
necessary concomitant of psychoanalysis. Thus:

[5] Heinz Hartmann, *Psychoanalysis and Moral Values* (New York: International Universities Press, 1960), p. 90.

To counteract a frequent misunderstanding, we do not expect an analyzed person to have no guilt feelings (we consider the capacity to experience guilt an entirely normal characteristic of human experience). But we expect that his guilt reactions will be more clearly in line with the integrated parts of his personality, with his authentic moral code, *and with the reality situations.* [Italics by author.]

Finally, Kohut and Seitz[6] state their view of the theoretical issue quite clearly and make it evident that the reality and value judgments of the analyst must of necessity be brought into play. They state as follows:

When anamnestic data from childhood or evidence from dreams point toward repressed material that has been contained effectively by socially acceptable and satisfactory defensive activities, no attempt is made to stir up such dormant conflicts during an analysis. If a violently hostile attitude towards a father figure has been superseded by devotion to a life task of promoting social justice for the aged, for example, there is no indication for attempting to undermine this ego-syntonic system of values unless neurotic inhibitions (due to a threatened breakthrough of the original hostility) interfere with this segment of psychic adjustment. Any walled-off content for which the defense mechanisms are securely anchored is thus left untouched. A perfectionistic attitude about uncovering the repressed is, at best, the sign of the amateur; at worst, it may betray the fanatic who, hiding some secret from himself, must forever wrest secrets from others.

Case Illustrations of the Use of Reality and Value Judgments

Since the ways in which the values held by the analyst become a part of the diagnostic and treatment situation are often subtle and readily rationalized, two fairly typical cases will be used as illustrative examples. In them the social judgments of the analyst come into play, and appraisals of average expectable environment and of

[6] Heinz Kohut and Phillip F. D. Seitz, "Concepts and Theories of Psychoanalysis," in *Concepts of Personality*, ed. Joseph M. Wepman and Ralph W. Heine (Chicago: Aldine Publ. Co., 1963), p. 130.

average expectable or adaptive behavior are made. Dependent on these, questions, clarifications, and interpretations are forthcoming. As will be demonstrated, even in the most nondirective of these, cueing, and reinforcement of certain valuative judgments occur as an inevitable and necessary part of the process.

The first patient is a business man in his mid-thirties who had come into treatment after the breakup of his marriage. His principal complaints were of feeling chronically mildly depressed, of some fears of being impotent if he established a relationship with another woman, and of great conflict and difficulty in dealing with his eight and ten year old sons with whom he had visitation privileges.

With regard to his family history and upbringing, he was the son of emigrant Jewish parents of Eastern European background. His father had, with considerable effort and much deprivation, graduated from dental school and, when the patient was born, he was already established in a modest but stable practice. Father appears to have been a mild-mannered rather passive man, much dominated by his wife. His office was in the home, and his avocation was cooking (at which he had become quite adept). He was rather distant and unrelated to the children as well as the patient could remember. He died in his mid-sixties of a sudden coronary thrombosis when the patient was twenty-three. His mother is now in her early seventies, and in good health other than a mild diabetes. She was the dominating member of the family, with some degree of scorn during the patient's growing up for what she considered to be his father's lack of appropriate aggressiveness and intellectual interests. Although she had some pretensions to intellectual interests herself, they were manifested in no tangible way. In addition to the patient there was one brother four years older, who—the patient always felt—overshadowed him. The brother was a good student, capable at athletics and greatly appreciated by the mother who saw in him many of the traits lacking in her husband. His brother took his doctorate in chemistry at a good university and is at present working at a fairly substantial job in industry in a town approximately fifty miles from their old home. He is also married and has three children.

The patient had a mediocre record in school and, in general, was relatively colorless during his formative years. While he can hardly have been said to have been neglected, mother's interests were intensely tied to older brother's accomplishments; the patient was the "baby." He received a share of things for just "being," and since little was expected of him—as he said—he did little. He went to a good college and did moderately well, but with no especial career direction. When a senior, he met his now-divorced wife who was also a student at the college and who—as he now says—"married him." Her family owned a large wholesale business in Baltimore, and on graduation from college he was taken into the business in a subordinate role. While his prospects were good, he was in no manner suited for the aggressive, hard-driving, competitive business tactics which were usual in the family and which were, in fact, fairly typical of the business in which the in-laws were engaged. During the early years of his marriage he remained in the family business, being carried more or less by sufferance and looked upon as the "weak sister." His wife, sharing the family values, was constantly exhorting him to be more aggressive—to be a man. When he was twenty-five, his first child was born, and at that time he found his role in business and at home insufferable. He somehow mobilized himself, set up a retail business in the same field, and to everyone's surprise—including perhaps his own—has been substantially successful in it. Paradoxically to him, despite his wife's prior exhortations, his new-found stature in life elicited not a better relationship with his wife but increased estrangement on her part, marked by irrational anger and sexual withdrawal. This finally culminated in divorce three years before he came into treatment. His wife simply left the home with the children and went to her mother's home to live.

As mentioned, in connection with the divorce proceedings which she insisted upon against his wishes, he was given visitation privileges each Sunday and this is the particular area on which we will focus during the remainder of this discussion. Time and again in the analytic sessions, the patient would talk about his difficulties in connection with these visits, as he found it extremely difficult to cope with his eight- and ten-year-old sons. They were constantly demanding things of him—that he take them here or there, bring them candy or ice-cream, play ball with them, etc. He left feeling exhausted and dispirited and unable to cope with the boys. He often felt like stopping the visits altogether; it intruded on his Sundays and he resented that. But then he didn't feel that it was right to neglect them—what kind of father would he be? (His own father had been neglectful of him and look what had happened to him!)

It is just here that some of the subtleties of the situation bear review. It would seem evident that this passive aggressive man finds himself engaged in conflict: between his inner feelings of love and hate for his children, his rational appraisal of their need for him and at the same time the major intrusion on his limited free time and the possibilities of creating a fuller life for himself, his identifications with his father and rejection of the implications of these identifications, his superego demand that he not desert his children and resultant guilt at the impulse to do so, and the perception— probably accurately—that his social group would see the rejection of them as a despicable act. In such a situation, depending on the factors of timing, his broader knowledge of numerous aspects of the case not mentioned in this brief report and his empathic sense of the situation, the analyst may behave in a variety of ways. It should be noted that the present focus is not on the matter of the actual impact of his behavior on the patient but on how it is that the psychotherapist or psychoanalyst behaves in certain ways and not others and the means through which he makes such judgments. The analyst may simply remain silent and listen, feeling that he does not have enough data or "feel" for the situation as yet; but even here is the suggestion that this is goal-directed and that at some future point in time such data, if available, will be put to some use. Any further behavioral pattern he may employ—including silence itself—deriving from other motivations (for instance that the patient is engaging in an attempt to manipulate the analyst as he once did his mother), represents a behavioral mode on the therapist's part based upon certain valuative judgments made by him.

Based upon the behavior of the "average expectable analyst" in our culture, it is likely that such explorations would be in the direction of his patient's continuing his visitations with his children rather than the opposite. Given ample room for the multi-determined nature of the problem the patient brings in, the silence of the analyst, questions intended to have the patient elaborate on his feelings about the situation with his children, explorations of the possibilities of genetic parallels in the way of sibling rivalry, oedipal conflicts, passivity problems, masochistic attitudes, libidinal attachments and so on the analyst, would operate on the first premise that the patient is not in an insufferable situation. The premise is that the patient is responding to an average expectable situation in one or more neurotic ways and that the visitation should be continued; that, in fact, his children's behavior towards him would probably modify favorably if he himself could behave differently.

Let us assume then, that the gamut of such behavior has been explored, that the analyst's judgment is that the adaptive capacities of the patient are greatly increased and that despite what appear to be most praiseworthy efforts on his part to deal with his children that their behavior remains the same or becomes even worse, based on factors not primarily related to him. At what point may the analyst then concur with the patient that this is not an average expectable environment and that in fact to continue the visits under the circumstances might itself be a neurotic and masochistic performance? Basically, it is perfectly evident that for the patient to stop his visits for healthy rather than for neurotic reasons is much to his advantage. In the process of the development of this issue, however, the analyst or therapist has first dealt with the internal conflict, and when he is satisfied that this is resolved his valuative appraisal of the environment must inevitably come into play.

The second case will perhaps even more blatantly illustrate this thesis. The patient is an attractive, single, young woman of twenty-eight who came for treatment because of the recurrence of a phobia for crowds and numerous psychosomatic manifestations in the way of palpitations, mild bouts of colitis, and a feeling of pressure in her epigastrium for which, after careful study, no organic basis could be found. She had had a similar period ten years before when her mother had a hysterectomy, and the symptoms had responded well to brief psychotherapy and medication.

The patient was born and brought up in a small southern town as the only child of a well respected minister. Her father was a somewhat severe man in his external manner but deeply attached to his work, and—to all appearance—to his wife and child as well. He was a handsome man and vigorous in manner and appearance even in his late sixties; he is still actively engaged in church work. The mother is described as a somewhat chronically depressed, rather cold person to whom the patient never felt very close. Much of the patient's early rearing was done by the "colored mammy," who is indeed still with the family. Mother did the jobs appropriate to a minister's wife—worked in the ladies' group of the church, did the proper entertaining, etc.—but life seemed to be a grim and serious business for her. The patient could not imagine her participating in sex much less enjoying it and wonders how it was that she ever married at all.

The patient recalls that in her childhood her main relationships were to "mammy" and her father. Mother was too busy seeing to it that things were immaculate in the house and attending to her church affairs. Evidently father poured a great deal of his tenderness and poorly sublimated sensuous needs into his relationship with his daughter. While there was nothing manifestly sexual in the relationship, there was a degree of physical closeness and of manner which might have been suggestive to another but was deeply repressed by both the patient and her father. When the patient was in her last year of high school her mother had a hysterectomy for fibroids and, in connection with it, the patient had her first flareup of the symptoms which brought her to treatment. As mentioned, she responded to treatment and went off to college at a small denominational school.

At college she got along satisfactorily, dated boys from a neighboring school, was fairly popular, and felt in no way different from the other girls. While at college she was preparing herself for educational work in the church and, on graduating at age twenty-two, came to Baltimore as educational director in a quite good parish. Throughout the years her relationship to the family has been—on the surface of things—good, and she often visits them and is visited by them.

When she was twenty-six, in connection with the church work she was thrown into extensive contact with a young minister whom she came to admire greatly. He was married, had three children, and seemed to be developing a good career. Stemming out of a rather casual flirtation at first, they found themselves greatly attracted to each other and ended up having an affair which was still continuing when she entered treatment. His life situation being what it was the prospects of their marrying were slim indeed, and yet they could not give each other up. She had many qualms of conscience about the relationship, often thought of disrupting it, but as many times felt drawn back when she saw him again. She was quite well aware that the tie to him was interfering with her meeting more eligible men and possibly marrying; she wished to have children but just could not interest herself in other men.

In such a situation the average expectable analyst would justifiably be impressed with the blatant oedipal nature of her familial relationship, with or without major preoedipal determining factors, depending on the further development of the case. The basic assumption would reasonably be that her relationship to the young minister was the consequence of her neurotic mode of relationship, and if treatment were successful that she might very well choose another mate. Generally, in fact, such a changed behavioral pattern is taken as strong evidence of successful treatment and a reduction of, or freedom from, neurosis and the continuation of the relationship to the minister as the opposite. The psychotherapist or psychoanalyst depends both upon cues from the patient and his own appraisal of the environment for his judgments. His participation is, in turn, dependent on these.

As was mentioned earlier, it is not uncommon for the analyst or the psychotherapist to side with the ego of the patient against the cruel and distorted superego and, indeed, in each of these cases the patients were self-accusatory and belittling of themselves in a moral sense—in the one instance for the resentment of an impulse to desert his children, in the other for the illicit affair. In both instances these self-recriminations simply helped to perpetuate a painful state of affairs and made for no constructive behavior. Such distortions of the superego functions may—and in the above mentioned case did—require analysis. Concomitantly with this, however, valuative appraisals based upon the degree of neurosis or the freedom from it, in part based upon an appraisal of the environment, are necessary. Such social appraisals include the moral and ethical climate of the culture and its probable responses to one sort of behavior or another, if the appraisal is to be reality-oriented and if adaptive behavior is to ensue.

Mental Health—Reality—and Values

The question of the role of social performance and of values in the concept of mental health has been dwelt upon extensively. As will be documented, the matter of whether mental illness is to be defined purely in intrapsychic terms, purely in social terms or in both, still remains highly controversial, with the psychoanalysts leaning more towards the former view. For instance, Lampl– DeGroot draws an analogy between bodily health, with its assimilation of stimuli from within and from without so as to maintain homeostasis, and mental health, where she sees the ego-organization and its synthesizing capacities in dealing with internal needs and external stimuli as being quite analogous. To her, judgments of health in terms of social performance are moral judgments and irrelevant to the scientific point of view.

Ruesch takes the opposite view and states, just as absolutely: "The nature of pathology implies the concept of health, and all medical and psychiatric thinking is geared towards helping the patient achieve health. Mental health is obviously defined in terms of the culture in which the patient and the therapist live."[7]

These two apparently totally incompatible points of view actually have a good deal in common. Lampl-DeGroot's "ego organization" derives not only from inner needs but also from a composite of cultural attitudes and pressures introjected substantially without conscious awareness in the form of attitudes deriving from the parents. The parents themselves have in turn, however, been subjected to these same pressures in the past. Once these attitudes have become assimilated they become a part of the person himself to a considerable extent at least. Ruesch is acutely aware of the cultural pressures but tends to de-emphasize the assimilative process and hence the internal conflictual nature of internalized cultural demands. As a result of their respective emphases each fails to put adequate emphasis on the other's point of view. As can be seen, this issue bears upon both the analyst's conceptualization of his role and his maneuvers in therapy to a degree but, as has been emphasized in the prior examples, does not exclude the use of his own reality testing and values in the analytic situation.

The Qualities of the Treating Person

The problem of the use of the reality and valuative capabilities of the analyst can be approached from yet another point of view.

[7] Jurgen Ruesch and Gregory Bateson, *Communication—the Social Matrix of Society* (New York: W. W. Norton and Co., 1951).

It is common parlance that an important requisite for the psycho-analyst is that he "must have lived." The particular characteristics which are implied by this term have much to do with the development and refinement of his ability to test reality and of his sense of values. Because of the evident bearing of this question upon the fundamental personality characteristics necessary in order to do psychoanalysis or psychotherapy, the underlying assumptions implied by the above phrase deserve elaboration.

As an approach to the problem, a relevant consideration by Ruesch[8] will be used. In it he states:

> The differences in the psychiatrist's value system from those of the core group arise from specific life experiences. Essentially they are related to experiences of culture contact and repeated exposure to differing systems of value during the formative years. Such conditions sharpen the social perception of the future psychiatrist and make him aware of the fact that values differ from group to group. Being forced to reinterpret his own position whenever he meets a new group, he develops the necessary means which enable him to perceive and evaluate the various communication systems of other people. Such basic life experiences are necessary if a man wishes to become a successful therapist. Training merely supplies a system for an orderly arrangement of these basic life experiences.

Ruesch seems to have in mind the development of the young psychiatrist, *de novo,* from those who choose this occupation. There is ample reason to believe that there are startling differences in aptitude in the applicants for psychoanalytic training based on their genetic experiences, modes of defense, and character structure in general. Technical development and education are important matters but not all persons are equally suitable for the task. The capacity to remain objective but at the same time to engage in the therapeutic situation asks for something more than developed technical skills. It is to say little of descriptive value simply to dismiss those who are felt to be unsuitable as being too rigid, narcissistic, infantile, or other cryptic terms of this sort. In evaluating candidates who would hope to become psychoanalysts or psychotherapists a not infrequently used referent, in addition to those of formal school-

---

[8] Ruesch and Bateson, *Communication—the Social Matrix of Society*, p. 20.

ing, etc., is the above-mentioned descriptive phrase, he "must have lived." Just what does this statement entail? Surely it cannot have reference only to a series of experiences which could be recorded by an objective observer, and in fact there seems to be no correlation between the degree of hardship in actuality, or the lack of it, and the degree to which the potential therapist possesses the quality under consideration. Neither the death of parents nor relatives, war nor famine nor good fortune seem in themselves to be the essential ingredients. The act of living itself brings to us all a sufficient supply of such experiences. We are not lacking in external stimuli; it is what we do with the stimuli in the way of incorporating them or defending against them that is the critical matter.

What impression does one get of the person who has lived? How does he seem to meet himself and deal with others in a fashion which is different than the person about whom this would not be said? What way do we have of describing the obverse of "must have lived"? What verbal and nonverbal or empathic means seem to communicate this message? It is not a factor of intelligence or the ability to learn in the formal sense of the term alone, but it is also the ability to empathically experience with another person. This develops as a product of fully experiencing living and of digesting one's own experiences. He who has lived has a sense of others as distinct persons other than himself because he experiences himself as a distinct entity. His awareness of the other person's capacity to experience and to feel derives from his own capacity to do so, and his sense of separateness permits him to know that another person may think and feel in his own unique fashion just as he is aware of his own uniqueness. This particular definition transcends what is usually encompassed by the notion of capacity to have object relationships in that it derives basically from the individual's concept of himself. He has been able to incorporate the life situations involving others in such a fashion as to strengthen and solidify his sense of himself and his own unique existence. He has developed the capacity to tolerate the separateness and loneliness which are the inevitable consequences of the above state. In so doing he has attained a measure of objectivity in relation to others and the ability to participate in interaction with them in such a way as to be able to tolerate the inevitable frustrations arising from conflicts of interests between persons. This parallels his ability to cope with the conflicting drives within himself.

The modes of communicating the message—"I have lived"—are more essentially nonverbal as well as including the nonverbal concomitants of speech. They are manifested in how he "meets the world," in his seeming degree of awareness of others, and in his capacity to engage in a communication situation with appropriate gratification to himself and the other person. Such a person possesses an introspective potential which likely derives from infantile and early childhood experiences as well as from the incalculables of his inherited characteristics. In the negative sense, such an individual suffers from no major spheres of repression based upon his inborn equipment, the accidents of his upbringing, and such modifications as he is able to bring about himself through his own self investigations and his own personal psychoanalysis. Such areas of repression would invite not only the intrusion of his own primary processes into his patients' efforts at self-modification, but would distort his own opportunity to use his own reality sense and value judgments in his appraisal of, and attempts to assist, the patient.

In all of the various definitions of mental health, the assumption is that the analyst is an objective observer. This is true with regard to his capacity to appraise both the balance between the various intrapsychic components of the patient as well as the patient's adaptive capacity to the environment. It is certainly true of the latter, insofar as it may throw light on intrapsychic process. If this is accepted as valid, the above-mentioned description of the traits of character of the analyst must be such as to permit him to make appropriate use of his reality testing and value judgments. His capacity to do his work thus depends not only on his freedom from neurosis and the possession of certain acquired technical skills. Certain modes of "seeing the world" are an essential part of his equipment if he is to be helpful to his patients.

The use of the reality and the value judgments of the analyst are essential contributions on his part to the taking of a history, the conducting of a mental examination, and the treatment process itself. While many analysts would take exception to this principle on theoretical grounds, they employ these faculties in their actual work with patients. Much of this derives from the assumption that certain traits of character are inevitably necessary in the treating person and, lacking uniqueness, the tendency has been to fail to subject them to careful study. An attempt has been made to clarify this issue through a consideration of the kinds of persons who are more likely to become capable therapists.

Depending upon the stage of the treatment process, the analyst may choose to behave in a variety of different ways. His choice of behavior all the way from silence, to elaborative questions, to clarifications, to interpretations, is determined by his appraisal of the nature and intensity of the patient's dynamic conflicts. Concurrently he must come to some decision as to the nature of the various mental institutions, which of them may be distorted, what his best estimate of the economics of the situation are, and how a more functional and adaptive person may be created. In the process of this the environment is also appraised by him and is one additional factor, along with the others, that enters into his estimate of personality function. Inevitably the analyst must use his judgment of the presence or absence of neurosis as a crucial factor in estimating the presence or absence of an average expectable environment since he cannot, by the nature of his work, make a first hand investigation of it.

Emphasis has been placed on the increasing freedom from neurosis on the patient's part, his consequent better reporting of reality, and his valid attempts to engage in adaptive behavior as cues by which the analyst makes reality and value judgments about the external environment, about reported past events, and about the sum total of the patient's experiences in living.

X

THE INTEGRATIVE POTENTIAL OF RECONSTRUCTIONS

The Nature of Reconstructions

In the earlier chapters there are a number of references to the ways in which historical data and the reconstruction of past events come into play in the treatment process. A synthesis of these various elements will be presented in this chapter since their value must, in the final analysis, rest upon their usefulness in the treatment of patients.

At the outset, the factors which make up a reconstruction in the ordinary course of treatment need definition. A reconstruction is composed of the memories of prior events along with the more or less complete affective reliving of those events in the present, in the setting of the relationship to a treating person. This relationship is composed both of the actualities of the patient's experience, based in his accurate perceptions, as well as in such experiences as he may have of the treating person which are based in transference phenomena. With regard to the latter, this is to say that the patient experiences the psychotherapist or psychoanalyst as if he were some significant person from his past and hence responds to him accordingly.

The treating person, in turn, engages in more than one mode of experiencing the patient. He not only experiences the patient in full reality sense but in addition he himself engages in regressive modes of experience which are under the control of his ego. This

140

has been described as free floating attention (cf. *Listening with the Third Ear*). Insofar as this controlled regression is within the awareness of the therapist it is a necessary and constructive part of his experience. Only when his regressions are unconscious and outside of his control may these have a considerable negative potential. The advantage of this "regression in the service of the ego" on the part of the therapist is that it allows him to empathize more fully with the patient and thus to give free play to his creative sense. It is necessary for him to develop and to use his creativity since, based on the available facts, a reconstruction is always the product of a creative act.

The emphasis placed upon the use of words in the treatment process derives from the fact that affective re-experiencing of remembered past events depends upon verbal and ideational process in order for such events to be conceptualized in a new and more constructive way. While this is generally true, there are, of course, important exceptions and these have been elaborated upon. Earlier in this volume words were shown to have a defensive function on occasion. In such instances they are used to avert maladaptive havioral performances. However, generally verbal exchange is a crucial aspect of the therapeutic process. The capacity to use verbal symbols makes the therapeutic process a way of re-experiencing old events in a new context and provides a means for developing new reaction patterns. Words and the symbolic process of thinking allow a certain distance from the events themselves and a degree of trial, feeling, and action, through the process of phantasy. This process is the preliminary to establishing new modes of behavior. Often the early conditioning experiences from which maladaptive behavior derives occurred when verbal process—and hence the ability more adequately to cope—was poorly established. Elements of such early experiences are a part of later screen imagery and, while the specific content of such early experiences is not remembered, the feeling tone of these experiences is deeply embedded. This feeling tone then attaches itself to later experiences, and the recalled experiences in treatment represent a combination of very early feeling tones and later associated experiences. All memories are to a very significant degree "screen memories," and the actual reported incident serves the function of "fleshing out" affective states from even earlier unrecalled experiences. Such feeling states are the basic elements which require modification in the emotional disorders. The integration of verbal and affective reconstructions of certain unique kinds is therapeutic, and the conditions in which this may occur deserve careful consideration.

Affect and Reconstruction

The role of affect as a crucial part of the historical process and of reconstruction has not been emphasized as much as it deserves, since it does not lend itself as well to formal discourse as does ideational process. Affect no doubt plays a crucial role in both what is recalled, how it is reconstructed, and how the reconstruction will be experienced. The way a reconstruction is experienced may in itself be the crucial issue in determining whether it is to play a constructive or destructive role in personality organization. A theoretically absolutely accurate reconstruction of a past event may evoke either bitter accusations and hate or sympathy and understanding, and this will determine how the patient will feel and behave.

The degree and nature of the affective state accompanying any recalled event are matters of great importance. The therapeutic process itself depends upon the coalition of remembered events with an affect appropriate to such events in the patient/therapist context. Much of the therapeutic process has to do with the attempts to bring about just such a state of affairs. The memory of some prior affective state may be the only recalled aspect of a significant experience, and this affective memory may be precipitated by a present experience. Other aspects of the past experience may simply not be recalled or some other plausible experience may be substituted instead. The recalled event with an appropriate affect carries with it, for both patient and therapist, a sense of conviction not otherwise experienced. This is often the condition for accepting the recalled experience as having actually transpired at some point in the past. Even where the reported past event and its associated affect do not appear congruent with reality to the therapist—as in the paranoid state—and no consensus can be arrived at with the patient, the reported event is real for the patient and may be experienced with intense affect. This is of some importance in listening to delusional reconstructions of history since such a perceptive attitude on the therapist's part makes for a potentially more helpful situation.

The Stereotypy of Experience and Behavior

Repetitious maladaptive functioning is characteristic of the neurotic and psychotic disorders. For any given person there is a fairly invariable pattern of defenses and drive characteristics which, taken together, constitute his character structure. Therefore, whether he is in an integrated state or less so, he will display patterns of behavior and a body of experiences which are typical for him. In his unique constitution and life experiences he has developed highly characteristic and stereotypical modes of response. This is so whether a highly integrated response is occurring or whether his particular modes of disintegration and disorganization are in process. Treatment attempts to alter these modes of response in a positive direction, and reconstructions are important instruments towards this end.

Reconstructions, based on the available history, are inevitably discontinuous, and however logically the pieces may be fitted together there are areas which rest more firmly on available data and other areas which are largely a product of the creative sense of both patient and physician. These latter are to a very large degree intelligent surmises of what "likely happened." This is not to say that such surmises should not be made or are not therapeutic in their effect. The historian who accepts the ambiguity and limitations of the reconstructive process is in a position to make more intelligent use of them, however.

Unless great care is exercised, the prejudices of the treating person may be substituted for those of the patient, and a consensus may be arrived at with the patient on the basis of this new system of prejudices. It is here that the attempt actually to reconstruct the precise nature of past events and not simply a plausible version of them becomes a matter of the first importance. In certain instances, determining as accurately as possible whether a given event actually transpired becomes a primary matter in psychiatry and psychoanalysis. While the matter of the memory of past events and their reorganization in therapy is always important, this is based on actual events of which it is important for the therapist to remain cognizant. While such events can never be totally re-examined, a careful study of the available evidence gives useful hints as to the characterological nature, modes of defense, and sources of emotional difficulty from which the patient suffers, and it is important in determining the therapeutic approach to the patient. The psychotherapist or psychoanalyst depends upon his general knowledge of the way people usually behave as well as upon his intuitive sense about a particular patient as aids in making reconstructions of the probable course of events in the patient's life. In such reconstructions—as is appropriate and in fact inevitable—he is influenced by his particular point of view and his interest in helping the patient. That the means of actual validation of prior events is limited should be recognized, but this by no means vitiates the importance of attempts at such validation, where appropriate, or of the historical approach to treatment.

The transference situation recreates in a present context some near facsimile of a past experience. This is so because the performance of the patient tends towards stereotypy, and this is especially so of neurotic forms of behavior. In the transference situation the patient experiences the therapist as being like some historical figure in his life and responds to him as such. The transference thus serves as a window into the past. While the original state of affairs cannot be recreated in its entirety, the affective situation is sufficiently of a kind with it to allow reasonable assumptions to be drawn. The therapeutic situation is perhaps as close as we can come to the actual recreation of an historical event. The regressive nature of the transference situation with the associated verbal preoccupation with historical events bears a considerable resemblance to certain classical conditioning experiments in animals. In these, stimuli which have long since ceased to produce the conditioned response will nevertheless produce autonomic visceral responses which may well be the physiological concomitants of emotion. Aided by man's verbal capacity, the historical event and its associated feelings are communicated in the therapeutic situation and re-experienced in a fashion which closely parallels the original event.

144

The Role of Internalization

Since the process of treatment itself goes on simultaneously with numerous other activities and experiences in the patient's life, these no doubt influence what is going on in the treatment and hence influence the state of mind of the patient during the course of his working out reconstructions. This affects the very content of the reconstructions themselves, although this is difficult to appraise and hence little attention has been paid to it. While exception might be taken to the above, notice the ease with which the proposition is accepted in reverse—namely that events in the treatment interview influence events in the life of the patient outside of it.

Reconstructions derive from a composite image of remembered prior events and of present actual events. This includes the patient's experiences of the treatment and of the treating person himself. In the treatment situation, the patient projects many aspects of his own experience, feeling, and imagery upon the treating person. By so doing, he has the opportunity to examine these aspects of himself, to organize them in a more constructive way, and finally to reinternalize them so as to regain a higher level of autonomy. In the treatment situation he recreates past modes of response and experience in miniature, albeit colored by the experiences and character changes of the intervening years up to the present. In so doing he gains a new outlook and new ways of dealing with old stereotypies.

The internalization of the treating person plays a significant role in the therapeutic process. The usual reconstruction of past events during the treatment process derives from the internalization of the psychotherapist's or psychoanalyst's perspectives, realities, and values along with such direct changes as may occur within the patient himself. The treating person helps the patient to see the world through his eyes and lends him his perspective while he is helping the patient develop his own. This is done through questions, interpretations, and the entire system of cueing devices discussed earlier in this book. The patient identifies with the psychoanalyst in many ways, and the analysis of the transference neurosis can hardly be said to be unsuccessful simply because of the persistence of these identifications.

The matter of identification and of internalization bears on the subject of reconstruction since the reconstruction of the memories of prior persons and events is done with the collaboration of the treating person. In addition, the treating person himself is internalized by the patient and becomes an inextricable part of the patient's conceptualization of past persons and events. The images reconstructed by the patient of significant persons from earlier in his life often bear a striking resemblance to the way in which he conceptualizes and experiences the treating person. This does not derive from transference and projection alone. It is also a product of actual perceptions of the treating person as he is. This is a major reason why the maturity and stability of the treating person is a matter of such importance. He must be not only the scientific observer and commentator but a fit subject for internalization as well.

The Problem of Validation of Reconstructions

The theories employed in dynamic psychiatry and psychoanalysis having to do with human development can be seen in fuller perspective and can be more intelligently used when the significance of reported memories are taken for what they are. As has been emphasized, the extent to which the patient's memory of these events actually coincides with events of the past is open to serious question. This is not to say that the data obtained from the patient about remembered past events is unimportant, but the meaning of psychiatric theories deriving from such data warrant clear definition.

Certain biases derive from the treating person as well as from the patient in appraising data having to do with remembered prior events. As has been mentioned, the data supplied by the patient is fitted into an a priori schema of human development by the treating person. This is done irrespective of the idiosyncratic specifics of this particular patient's experiences. This allows the data to be categorized in an orderly manner. The schema employed derives from a variety of sources. Included are theories deriving from poeple who have conducted prior processes such as these, observing the reported memories of former patients of his own, his own introspections and introspections he may share with other persons.

146

The patient, in turn, employs the same mechanisms in reporting past events as he is in the habit of employing in connection with reported present events. These include all of the classic modes of defending against anxiety such as denial, repression, projection, and so on. Of course, as the treating person becomes more familiar with the patient's modes of defense and as the patient's need for such defenses decreases, a somewhat more accurate recall might be expected. How to validate such memories and the subsequent theory-making and reconstructions still remains a knotty problem.

For purposes of illustration, if 100 patients with obsessional neuroses claimed to have memories of having been kicked in the "backside" at the age of three, the following means of validation of the relevance of the kick to the formation of obsessional neurosis would be available. These are: (1) reports of the memory of the patient (2) longitudinal studies of groups of people who have been so kicked (3) reports from the kickers who can supply independent memories that the kicking actually happened, and (4) experimentally kicking one half of a group of three-year-olds and seeing if this group had a higher incidence of obsessional neuroses than did the control group. The fact of the matter is that while some longitudinal studies are in progress, practically all of the a priori theoretical formulations employed in clinical practice derive from the first group, the reported memory of the patient. It is thus from this group that the basic theory and the reconstructions commonly employed derive.

Reconstructions are inevitably made from the point of view of the person making them, and they are influenced by what he intends to do with them. This is especially so when the process involves reconstructing not only the actual physical events of the past but, more especially, the psychological status of the participants in events of the past. Since this latter is the very meat of the reconstructive process in psychiatry and psychoanalysis, reconstructions are heavily influenced by one's theoretical position and one's feeling for what will be most useful therapeutically. There is, in the final analysis, no "true" reconstruction; there are reconstructions of greater or lesser degree of validity and plausibility and, most importantly, greater or lesser degrees of usefulness as integrative forces.

The Value of Reconstructions

Reconstructions of past events which are accepted by the patient and become a part of his identity and of his character structure can be said to have a quality of genuineness whether or not they coincide with the actual course of prior events. The original past events were experienced within the perceptual scope of the patient and were influenced, if not actually determined, by his affective state at the time. Optimally, this is what one might ultimately obtain even in a theoretically perfect reconstruction. The genuineness in that case would derive from its correspondence to a far greater degree with the nature of the patient's experience and only to a much lesser degree with the actuality of events as viewed in the abstract. In this sense the convincing reconstruction in treatment is always a genuine event and is so treated by the patient and the treating person as well.

Since the patient's personal identity is intimately tied to his inner experience of and associated recall of his parents and others, the therapist, with or without specific awareness, often becomes a party to recreating, with the patient's help, a modified image of the parents. The goal in such instances is to modify inner imagery (in a helpful way) in such a fashion as to contribute to present modes of living. While there are many who would prefer to ignore it, the fact is that the modified image is hardly more validatable than was the original one. Such reconstructions are often considered sacrosanct and as being above proof and requiring no proof. This is the implication of such statements as "analysis showed thus and so" where analysis itself is offered as the validation of the very events it is said to have revealed. By means of conscious planning, the therapist can modify history purely for its therapeutic effect and, given reasonable plausibility, it may assist the patient in adopting a more useful view of historical figures in his life. The primary interest here is not in validating a historical figure in any absolute sense, if this could be done, but in creating an historical figure of use to the patient. It should not be assumed that what is being suggested is an inevitable glorification of the parent in the hope that the patient can identify with this more constructive image. Thus if the patient is felt to have identified himself with a latently psychotic parent and is living out the "crazy role," a reconstruction which reveals the parent's aberration may be the means by which the patient separates himself and becomes better integrated in the process. If, on occasion, the image of parent aberration is overdrawn by the therapist this may perhaps be excused if the result itself is a therapeutic one.

Reconceptualizing his world, including his self percept, will eventuate in different modes of experiencing and feeling on the patient's part. This will manifest itself in his modes of behavior and thus of relating to other persons. How he experiences his curriculum vitae, based on his reconstructions of past events, is critical to the way he will see himself and those about him in the present and in the future. Since his present sense of himself will affect present performance, a more constructive self image will make for a greater likelihood of reinforcing experiences from others of a positive nature. Just so, a negative self image and its accompanying affects will make for negative reinforcements from others.

The impact of reconstructions and hence of the way one's past is seen cannot be overestimated as a force in determining the course of future events. The very concept of history as a predictive instrument suggests that today's view of history will influence tomorrow's course of events. The existence of optimistic or pessimistic outlooks is significantly based on the appraisal of past events, and such mood states bear considerably on what will actually happen tomorrow. This is no magical formula but simply a statement that, aside from accidents of fate, the patient's capacities for adaptation, significantly based on his appraisal of past events, will have a major influence on the course of his future.

GLOSSARY

AMNESIA

The inability to recall past experiences.

ANAMNESIS

In medicine this commonly refers to the historical account of a patient's life antedating the period of the present illness.

BORDERLINE STATES

Disturbed states in which patients are not psychotic and can function in the community, but might easily become psychotic.

CATATONIA

The clinical syndrome called catatonia is characterized as a rule by (1) stupor, associated with either marked rigidity or flexibility of the musculature, or (2) overactivity.

COMPULSIVE–DEPRESSIVE PERSONALITY

This term does not appear in standard psychiatric dictionaries. Presumably, it refers to a personality with compulsive and depressive tendencies (see below). It is known that people who become depressed in middle or late life frequently have had compulsive personalities for many years prior to their depression.

COMPULSIVE PERSONALITY

This refers to an individual who has a severe super-ego (see below) and who tends to be perfectionistic, rigid, and excessively responsible and dutiful. In extreme form, these traits can make it difficult for the individual to make decisions or to work. However, when present in an otherwise normal personality, such traits can lead to excellence of work and strength of character.

CONDENSATION

The compression of many ideas or allied experiences into a single thought or word.

150

DEPRESSIVE PERSONALITY	This refers to a person who chronically experiences depression, an affective feeling-tone which may vary from a mild down-heartedness or feeling of indifference to hopeless despair. In the mild depressive syndrome, the patient is quiet, restrained, self-depreciative, and has a feeling of inadequacy and discouragement. He is unable to make decisions and experiences difficulty with usually easy mental activities.
COUNTER–TRANSFERENCE	See *Transference*.
DEFENSE	Any psychological mechanism by which the ego automatically protects the personality against anxiety, shame, or loss of self-esteem. For example, projection of self-blame on to another individual.
DÉJÀ VU	A new scene that gives the illusion of familiarity.
DISPLACEMENT	This refers to the transference of emotions from the original ideas to which they are attached to other ideas.
DYNAMIC PSYCHIATRY	Any psychiatric theory which recognizes that present behavior is based on all that has gone before in the psychic life of the individual, and that it is a result of opposing drives and motives. Dynamic psychiatry is often looked upon as using the knowledge derived from psychoanalytic studies.
ECONOMIC VIEWPOINT	That part of psychoanalytic theory which is concerned with the origin, distribution, and consumption of psychic energy.
FOLIE À DEUX	A condition in which two persons closely associated with one another share delusions or a delusional system, and one member of the pair appears to have influenced the formation of delusions in the other.
FUGUE	In psychiatry this means a flight, so to speak, from reality in which the individual seems to possess all of his mental faculties, but questioning may reveal complete or partial amnesia for certain experiences.

HYSTERICAL CONVERSION	The manifestation of a bodily symptom, such as paralysis or anesthesia, as a result of unconscious psychic conflict. This is also referred to as "hysteria" and "conversion reaction."
HYSTERICAL PHOBIC DISORDER	This is another name which is not to be found in a standard list of psychiatric disorders. Presumably, Dr. Novey referred to a disorder with both hysterical and phobic features, like Freud's "anxiety hysteria."
ID	That division of the mind from which come blind, impersonal, instinctual impulses that press for immediate gratification of primitive needs.
IDENTIFICATION	When an individual, by incorporating within himself a mental picture of an object, thinks, feels, and acts as he conceives the object to think, feel, and act, the process is called identification. It is largely an unconscious process.
INTERNALIZATION	This word is often used synonymously with identification.
MANIC–DEPRESSIVE	A psychotic state characterized by alternating episodes of euphoria with overactivity, and profound melancholy. The individual may appear quite normal in between these episodes. If the recurrent episodes are only those of mania, the illness is still called manic-depressive.
MENTAL INSTITUTIONS	This phrase refers to the three principal "structures" of the mind in Freudian theory: the id, the ego, and the super-ego.
OBSESSIVE– COMPULSIVE NEUROSIS	A form of emotional illness characterized by the presence of irresistible ideas or impulses. It may appear as an extreme form of the personality described above as compulsive.
PARESIS	A psychiatric disorder characterized by both mental and physical symptoms. It is due to syphilis of the central nervous system.
PRECONSCIOUS	Not present in consciousness at a given moment, but more-or-less readily recallable when wanted.

PSYCHOANALYSIS

A type of treatment in which the purpose is to gain access to thoughts and feelings of the patient, which have been repressed, to a more extensive degree than is possible in the various psychotherapies. The purpose is a reorganization of those aspects of the patient's behavior which have led to serious difficulties in living. For this purpose, the therapeutic situation is structured in such a way as to facilitate the recollection of dreams and of unconscious material—i.e., the patient is instructed to say whatever comes to mind, the analyst is not within the patient's direct view, and the patient comes 4 to 6 times a week. An essential feature of this treatment is that the therapist has had long theoretical and practical training in understanding and dealing with the thoughts and feelings thus produced.

PSYCHOTHERAPY

A type of psychiatric treatment which often uses psychoanalytic principles as its basis, but with often more limited goals in mind. It is usually thought of as a type of psychiatric treatment in which the patient sees the doctor with less frequency than he does in psychoanalysis and usually the therapist is within easy view of the patient.

REGRESSION IN THE SERVICE OF THE EGO

This occurs when an individual feels and behaves with less than his usual maturity in the interest of loosening up a fixed pattern for the purpose of reorganization and reintegration of the personality.

REIFY

To treat an abstract concept or construct as if it had a concrete existence.

RESISTANCE

Opposition to any attempt to lay bare the content of the unconscious. This may, for example, take the form of difficulty in speaking, failure to appear for sessions, or abrupt termination of treatment.

SCHIZOID

An enduring pattern of behavior manifesting avoidance of close relations with others, and an inability to express hostility and aggressive feelings directly.

153

SCHIZOPHRENIA

A group of psychotic reactions characterized by fundamental disturbances in reality relationships in a conceptual world determined excessively by primitive ideation. Marked affective-intellectual and overt behavioral disturbances are frequently present, including hallucinations and delusions and behavioral responses to them.

SUPER-EGO

A system of the mind developed by incorporating parental standards or, somewhat more broadly, by incorporating the moral standards of society.

TRANSFERENCE

Thoughts and feelings formerly directed toward someone in one's life (e.g., parents) which are now directed toward someone in one's present experience (e.g., the therapist). These thoughts and feelings are ordinarily repressed but may become conscious during therapy.

Counter-transference. Similar thoughts and feelings on the part of the therapist which are aroused by the therapeutic situation and are directed toward the patient.

BIBLIOGRAPHY

Anderson, John E. 1950. Changes in emotional response with age. In *Moosehart Symposium*. New York: McGraw Hill.

Arlow, Jacob. 1955. The structure of déjà vu. *J. Amer. Psychoanal. Ass.* 7:611–31.

Brody, E. B. 1960. Borderline state, character disorder, and psychotic manifestations—some conceptual formulations. *Psychiatry* 23:75–80.

Ekstein, R., and Rangell, L. 1961. Reconstruction and theory formation. *J. Amer. Psychoanal. Ass.* 9(4):684–97.

Federn, Paul. 1952. *Ego Psychology and the Psychoses.* New York: Basic Books.

Fenichel, Otto. 1945. *The Psychoanalytic Theory of Neuroses*, pp. 295ff. New York: W. W. Norton and Co.

Ferenczi, Sandor. 1911. *Obscene Words in Sex and Psychoanalysis*, pp. 132–53. New York: Robert Brunner, 1950.

————. 1916. *Papers on Psychoanalysis.* Boston: Badger and Co.

Fisher, Charles, and Paul, I. H. 1959. The effect of sublimal visual stimulation on images and dreams: a validation study. *J. Amer. Psychoanal. Ass.* 7:35–83.

Frankl, Viktor. 1963. *Man's Search for Meaning.* New York: Beacon Press.

Freud, Sigmund. 1920. Beyond the Pleasure Principle. *Complete Psychological Works of Sigmund Freud*, standard ed. 12:35–37. London: Hogarth Press, 1958.

————. 1920. *General Introduction to Psychoanalysis*, p. 323. New York: Garden City Publishing Co.

————. 1911. Formulations on the Two Principles of Mental Functioning. *Complete Psychological Works of Sigmund Freud*, standard ed. 12:218–30. London: Hogarth Press, 1958.

————. 1915. Instincts and Their Vicissitudes. *Complete Psychological Works of Sigmund Freud*, standard ed. 14: 117–40. London: Hogarth Press, 1957.

————. 1917. Mourning and Melancholia. *Collected Papers of Sigmund Freud* 4:152–70. London: Hogarth Press, 1946.

155

BIBLIOGRAPHY

————. 1898. My Views on the Part Played by Sexuality in the Etiology of Neuroses. *Collected Papers* 1:279. London: Hogarth Press, 1947.

————. 1917. Notes upon a Case of Obsessional Neurosis. *Complete Psychological Works,* standard ed. 17: 61–71. London: Hogarth Press, 1955.

————. 1899. Screen Memories. *Complete Psychological Works,* standard ed. 3:303–22. London: Hogarth Press, 1951.

Garraty, John A. 1957. *The Nature of Biography.* New York: A. A. Knopf.

Glover, E. 1939. The psychoanalysis of affects. *Int. J. Psychoanal.* 20: 299–307.

Goddard, K. E., Broder, G., and Wenar, C. 1961. Reliability of pediatric histories, a preliminary study. Special article, *Pediatrics* 28(6):1011–18.

Gould, Roger L., and Nahum, Alan M. 1966. Psychological motivations in stapes surgery. *Trans. Amer. Acad. Ophthal. Otolaryng.* May–June:398–403.

Greenacre, Phyllis. 1950. General problems of acting out. *Psychoanal. Quart.* 19:455–67.

Haggard, E. A., Brekstad, A., and Skard, A. G. 1960. On the reliability of the anamnestic interview. *J. Abnorm. Soc. Psychol.* 61(3):311–18.

Haron, W., Bexton, W. H., and Hebb, D. C. 1953. Cognitive effects of a decreased variation in the sensory environment. *Amer. Psych.* 8(8).

Hartmann, Heinz. 1958. *Ego Psychology and the Problem of Adaptation.* New York: International Universities Press.

Hebb, Donald G. 1949. *The Organization of Behavior.* New York: John Wiley.

Hollingworth, H. L. 1930. *Abnormal Psychology.* New York: Ronald Press.

Kennan, George F. 1954. *Realities of American Foreign Policy,* pp. 3–30. Princeton, N.J.: Princeton University Press.

Kernberg, Otto. 1965. Notes on countertransference. *J. Amer. Psychoanal. Ass.* 13(1): 38–56.

Lampl–DeGroot, Jeanne. 1963. Symptom formation and character formation. *Int. J. Psychoanal.* 44:1–11.

Lewin, B. D. 1950. *The Psychoanalysis of Elation.* New York: W. W. Norton.

Lilly, John C. 1956. Illustrative strategies for research in psychopathology in mental health. In *Symposium 2, Group for the Advancement of Psychiatry.*

————. 1956. Mental effects of ordinary levels of physical stimuli on intact, healthy persons. In *Psychiatric Research Reports 5, Amer. Psychoanal. Ass.* 5:1–9.

MacFarlane, V. W. 1938. Studies in child guidance: (1) methodology of data collection and organization. *Monogr. Res. Child. Develop.* 3(6).

BIBLIOGRAPHY

McGhie, A., and Chapman, J. S. 1964. Disturbance in selective attention in schizophrenia. *Proc. Roy. Soc. Med.* 57:419–22.

Mendelson, Myer. 1960. *Psychoanalytic Concepts of Depression,* p. 170. Springfield, Ill.: C. C Thomas.

Meyerhoff, Hans. 1959. *The Philosophy of History in Our Time.* New York: Doubleday and Co.

Morris, Charles W. 1946. *Signs, Language, and Behavior.* Englewood Cliffs, N.J.: Prentice-Hall.

Muncie, W. 1960. Clinical importance of overt and hidden depression. *Rhode Island Med. J.* 43(2):95–99.

Novey, Samuel. 1959. A clinical view of affect theory in psychoanalysis. *Int. J. Psychoanal.* 40:1–11.

————. 1962. The principle of 'working through' in psychoanalysis. *J. Amer. Psychoanal. Ass.* 10(4):658–76.

————. 1955. The role of the superego and ego-ideal in character formation. *Int. J. Psychoanal.* 36:254–59.

————. 1937. Utilization of social institutions as a defense technique in the neuroses. *Int. J. Psychoanal.* 38(2):82–91.

Penfield, W., and Rasmussen, T. 1950. *The Cerebral Cortex in Man,* p. 164. New York: Macmillan Co.

Rapaport, D., and Gill, M. 1959. The points of view and assumptions of metapsychology. *Int. J. Psychoanal.* 40:153–61.

Raymond, Charles K. 1963. Anxiety and task as determiners of verbal performance. *J. Exp. Psychol.* 46(2):120–24.

Reich, W. 1949. Conditions of character differentiation. In *Character Analysis,* 3d ed. New York: Orgone Institute Press.

Reik, Wilhelm. 1949. *Listening with the Third Ear.* New York: Farrar, Straus, and Co.

Ruesch, Jurgen, and Bateson, Gregory. 1951. *Communication—the Social Matrix of Psychiatry.* New York: W. W. Norton and Co.

Rycroft, Charles. 1937. The nature and function of the analyst's communication to the patient. *Int. J. Psychoanal.* 37:469–72.

Schachtel, E. 1949. *On Memory and Childhood Amnesia, a Study of Interpersonal Relations,* ed. P. Mullahy, pp. 3–49. New York: Hermitage Press.

Serota, Herman M. 1964. Home movies of early childhood: correlative developmental data in the psychoanalysis of adults. *Science* 143-(3611):1195.

Shand, Alexander. 1914, 1920. *The Foundation of Character,* p. 50. New York and London: Macmillan.

Silverman, J. 1964. The problem of attention in research and theory in schizophrenia. *Psychol. Rev.* 71:352–79.

Stern, A. 1945. Psychoanalytic therapy in the borderline neuroses. *Psychoanal. Quart.* 14:190–98.

Stern, Fritz. 1959. *The Philosophy of History in Our Time.* New York: Doubleday and Co.

BIBLIOGRAPHY

Usdansky, G., and Chapman, L. J. 1960. Schizophrenic-like responses in normal subjects under time pressure. *J. Abnorm. Soc. Psychol.* 60:143–46.

Waelder, R. 1936. The principle of multiple function. *Psychoanal. Quart.* 5:45–62.

Walker, R. E., and Spence, Janet Taylor. 1964. Relationship between digit span and anxiety. *J. Consult. Psychol.* 28(3):220–23.

Walsh, W. H. 1960. *Philosophy of History*. New York: Harper Torchbooks.

Whitehorn, J. C. 1939. Physiological changes in emotional states. *J. Ass. Res. Nerv. Ment. Dis.* 19:256.

Whorf, Benjamin Lee. 1956. *Language, Thought, and Reality: Selected Writings of Benjamin Lee Whorf.* New York: M.I.T. and John Wiley.

Yates, Aubrey V. 1966. Psychological deficit. *Ann. Rev. Psychol.* 17.

INDEX